The GLASGOW HERALD Scots Quiz Book.

by Lindsay MacDonald

BBC Scotland's reigning SUPERSCOT TV Quiz Champion

ISBN 0-948403-02-0

Bankhead
Annan Water
MOFFAT
DG10 9LS
Tel: 0683-20916

Designed by Associates, Lockerbie
Typeset by Nevisprint Limited, Fort William
Printed by Biddles Ltd, Guildford

The author would like to thank Lewis Macdonald, Sandy Bremner and the Rev. Roderick Macdonald for their help with some of the questions.

Photo credit on page 4: Jim Love

CONTENTS

Page

INTRODUCTION

We Scots are an educated race, or so we like to think. But when I won BBC Scotland's Superscot title on television last year I realised that I still had a lot to learn. Who was Robert Burns' favourite poet? Where do you find the island called the "Dutchman's Cap"? Who built Tobermory? Which Scots scientist did Einstein revere most of all? Not so easy, is it?

The Glasgow Herald Scots Quiz Book is the result of my desire to create an entertaining and informative quiz book for Scots of all ages, and so in Game 1 it starts relatively easily — we all know where Celtic won the European Cup, don't we? But by Game 10 the 999 questions under their repeating subject headings of *Great Scot!, Modern Scotland, Establishments, Sport, Highlands & Islands, History, From a' the Airts* and finally, *The Lowlands* should be giving you all cause for deep thought. The book is ideally formatted for teams of contestants, as in a pub quiz, or for pairs or just to quiz yourself.

Once you've worked your way through to Game 11, you can have a go at winning a case of Dalmore 12 year old malt whisky! Just to make it a little tougher, I've created three new sections in that game — *Scots Abroad, Spoken About Scotland* and *What's in a Name?* The final three questions are on a coupon to which you simply add your answers and pop it in the post. The winner will be drawn by me on the 29th December 1987, just in time for Hogmanay. Good luck!

Lindsay Macdonald

GREAT SCOT!

GAME 1

1 Which Glasgow-born thriller writer, author of *The Guns of Navarone,* died in February 1987?

2 Which poet burst on to the literary scene with the publication of the *Kilmarnock Edition*?

3 Which disc jockey left BBC Radio Scotland in 1984 to take over the *Breakfast Programme* on BBC Radio 2?

4 When is St Andrew's Day?

5 The editor of the *New York Herald* sent Henry Stanley into darkest Africa in pursuit of which Scot?

6 Who wrote *Sunset Song*?

7 Which saint's symbol is used in the Scottish flag?

8 Mary Queen of Scots was the queen of another country before Scotland — which one?

9 Who is credited with inventing the television?

10 . . . and who invented the pedal bicycle?

11 Which music hall star wrote an autobiography called *Roamin' in the Gloamin'*?

12 . . . and who wrote two volumes of autobiography called *The Moon's a Balloon* and *Bring on the Empty Horses*?

SECTION 2

MODERN SCOTLAND

GAME 1

13 In 1982, more than 250,000 admirers packed into Glasgow's Bellahouston Park to see who?

14 Who had a number one hit in 1979 with *One Day at a Time*?

15 Which city was chosen in 1986 to be the European City of Culture, 1990?

16 Which political party have held the majority of Scottish seats in Parliament since 1959?

17 Which is Scotland's oldest New Town?

18 . . . and which is the newest, established in 1966?

19 An inquiry was held in 1986 into the planned reprocessing plant for Europe's nuclear waste. Where was it to be built?

20 A spate of suicides at which youth penal complex in the 1980s led to demands for its closure?

21 In which film did Sean Connery make his comeback as James Bond, in 1983?

22 . . . and his son Jason Connery took over the title role in which TV series three years later?

23 Which body was established in 1965 by an Act of Parliament to promote the economic prosperity of the North of Scotland?

24 . . . and which organisation was set up by the government 10 years later to aid industry and attract investment in the Scottish economy?

SECTION 3

ESTABLISHMENTS

GAME 1

25 The couthy TV series *Beechgrove Garden* is one of BBC Scotland's most successful programmes. Where is the Beechgrove Garden?

26 Where have Daphne Brown, PC Murdoch and Hon Man lived as neighbours for decades?

27 In which building does Scotland's supreme civil court, the Court of Session, sit?

28 What is the name of the Church of Scotland's major annual conference?

29 Name the sister paper to the *Sunday Mail*.

30 Dundee has earned a reputation for Jute, Jam and Journalism. Which company employs most of the journalists?

31 What do William Grant and William Teacher make?

32 What is the name of Scotland's Anglican Church?

33 In which town is the Museum of Childhood?

34 . . . and the West Highland Museum?

35 Where are the headquarters of the Lothian Regional Council?

36 . . . and of Highland Regional Council?

SECTION 4

SPORT

GAME 1

37 Who became the world's youngest snooker professional in 1985?

38 In which town is the famous Coasters indoor Sports arena?

39 Which football team provided all the players for the Scottish team in the first-ever clash with England in 1872?

40 Which cyclist won the King of the Mountains title in the 1984 Tour de France?

41 Which is the home town of Raith Rovers Football Club?

42 In which sport do Scotland play England each year for the Calcutta Cup?

43 In which town is golf played on courses called Old, New, Eden and Jubilee?

44 Which Highland games is annually attended by members of the Royal Family?

45 Where did Celtic win the European Cup in 1967?

46 . . . and where did Aberdeen win the Cup-Winners Cup in 1983?

47 Which race course is the setting for the Scottish Grand National?

48 . . . and which one, in January 1987, became the first new jump course since the 1960s?

SECTION 5

THE HIGHLANDS & ISLANDS

GAME 1

49 Where is Sumburgh airport?

50 Which island is known as the Misty Isle?

51 Which species of squirrel is commonest in the Highlands?

52 Where is Paul McCartney's Highland estate?

53 What type of shooting trophy is the head of a red deer stag with 12 points to its antlers?

54 What is the main ingredient of Cullen Skink — fish, beef or bacon?

55 Which part of modern Scotland became part of Great Britain in 1955?

56

Of the three men's fate we found no trace
Of any kind in any place
But a door ajar and an untouched meal
And an overtoppled chair

Wilfred Wilson Gibson's poem tells of the mysterious disappearance in 1900 of three keepers from which remote island lighthouse?

57 On the shore of which loch stands Inveraray?

58 . . . and Ullapool?

59 Scotland's islands have been inhabited for thousands of years. Where is the prehistoric village of Skara Brae?

60 . . . and Jarlshof?

SECTION 6

HISTORY

GAME 1

61 England may have been the "auld enemy", but who were Scotland's partners in the "auld alliance"?

62 Who were known as "resurrectionists" or "anatomies" in the early 19th century?

63 Which city owed much of its expansion to the tobacco lords?

64 When did the Union of Parliaments of England and Scotland occur?

65 Place in chronological order: Mary Queen of Scots, Robert the Bruce and James VI.

66 Who was the mother of Mary Queen of Scots?

67 The first half of the 17th Century saw the "plantation" of 40,000 Scottish settlers in which country?

68 Whom did the monks of Iona refer to as "the gentiles"?

69 Where are the Scottish Crown Jewels kept?

70 . . . and where is the ancient throne of Scottish kings, the Stone of Destiny?

71 Which clan traditionally held the title of Lords of the Isles?

72 . . . and which island was their power-base?

SECTION 7

FROM A' THE AIRTS

GAME 1

73 When is the Selkirk Grace traditionally spoken?

74 What is the better-known name of the play *The Boy Who Never Grew Up*?

75 What kind of musical instrument is a clarsach?

76 Which popular folksong chorus begins with the line:

O gin ye were whaur the Gadie rins?

77 Which sacred song became a number one hit when played by the pipe band of the Royal Scots Dragoon Guards?

78 Which famous musical centred on a Highland community which came to life once every 100 years?

79 Who wrote the book *Ring of Bright Water*?

80 Popular singers Des O'Connor and Roger Whittaker had a Hogmanay hit with which folksong in 1986?

81 In which city is the Graigmillar Festival held?

82 . . . and the Easterhouse Festival?

83 In which city is the Tron Theatre?

84 . . . and His Majesty's Theatre?

SECTION 8

THE LOWLANDS

GAME 1

85 One of Britain's principal breeding grounds of gannets is a rock in the Firth of Clyde. What is its name?

86 Which town has railway stations called Central and Queen Street?

87 Which border town is known as the "Muckle Toon"?

88 Holiday resorts on the banks of which river are described as being "doon the watter"?

89 To which Dumfriesshire village do runaway couples traditionally elope?

90 Who is "Auld Clootie"?

91 In which of Scotland's old counties was Glasgow situated?

92 The Ayrshire village of Dunlop has given its name to what type of food?

93 In Glasgow, what is the "Clockwork Orange"?

94 . . . and what are the "Barrows"?

95 Which fish is cured to make an Arbroath Smokie?

96 . . . and which fish helps make up Tweed Kettle?

GAME 1
ANSWERS

·GREAT SCOT!·

1 Alistair MacLean.
2 Robert Burns (in 1786).
3 Ken Bruce.
4 November 30th.
5 The explorer, David Livingstone.
6 Lewis Grassic Gibbon.
7 St Andrew.
8 France (where she was the wife of Francis II).
9 John Logie Baird (in 1925).
10 Kirkpatrick Macmillan (in 1839).
11 Harry Lauder.
12 David Niven.

·MODERN SCOTLAND·

13 Pope John Paul II.
14 Lena Martell.
15 Glasgow.
16 Labour.
17 East Kilbride (1947).
18 Irvine (in Ayrshire).
19 Dounreay (in Caithness).
20 Glenochil (in Alloa).
21 *Never Say Never Again.*
22 *Robin of Sherwood.*
23 The Highlands & Islands Development Board.
24 The Scottish Development Agency.

GAME 1
ANSWERS

·ESTABLISHMENTS·

25 Aberdeen (in the grounds of the BBC station).
26 On the pages of the *Sunday Post.*
27 Parliament House in Edinburgh.
28 The General Assembly.
29 *The Daily Record.*
30 DC Thomson.
31 Whisky.
32 The Episcopal Church.
33 Edinburgh.
34 Fort William.
35 Edinburgh.
36 Inverness.

·SPORT·

37 Stephen Hendry (he was 16).
38 Falkirk.
39 Queen's Park (the score was 0-0).
40 Robert Millar (from Glasgow).
41 Kirkcaldy.
42 Rugby Union.
43 St Andrews.
44 Braemar.
45 Lisbon, Portugal.
46 Gothenburg, Sweden.
47 Ayr.
48 Musselburgh.

GAME 1 ANSWERS

·THE HIGHLANDS & ISLANDS·

49 The Shetland Isles.
50 The Isle of Skye.
51 The red squirrel.
52 The Mull of Kintyre.
53 A Royal head.
54 Fish.
55 Rockall (a tiny outcrop, 55 miles from the mainland).
56 Flannan Islands (15 miles west of Lewis).
57 Loch Fyne.
58 Loch Broom.
59 The Orkney Isles.
60 The Shetland Isles.

·HISTORY·

61 France (from 1195 - 1560).
62 Those who robbed graves to supply medical specimens.
63 Glasgow (a great 18th-century tobacco trading centre).
64 1707.
65 Robert the Bruce, Mary Queen of Scots, James VI.
66 Mary of Guise (also known as Mary of Lorraine).
67 Ulster.
68 The Vikings.
69 Edinburgh Castle.
70 Westminster Abbey.
71 The Macdonalds.
72 Islay.

GAME 1 ANSWERS

·FROM A' THE AIRTS

73 At Burns Suppers.
74 *Peter Pan* by JM Barrie.
75 A harp.
76 *At the Back o'Bennachie* (a mountain in Aberdeenshire).
77 *Amazing Grace* (in 1972).
78 *Brigadoon* (in 1954).
79 Gavin Maxwell.
80 *The Skye Boat Song.*
81 Edinburgh.
82 Glasgow.
83 Glasgow.
84 Aberdeen.

·THE LOWLANDS·

85 Ailsa Craig.
86 Glasgow.
87 Langholm.
88 The River Clyde.
89 Gretna.
90 The Devil (a cloot being a hoof).
91 Lanarkshire.
92 Cheese.
93 The underground railway (the trains are orange).
94 A market, where the goods were once displayed in barrows.
95 Haddock.
96 Salmon.

SECTION 1

GREAT SCOT!

GAME 2

97 Who was born Marie McDonald McLaughlin Lawrie?

98 Which standard unit of power is named after a Scottish engineer?

99 Who wrote *Whisky Galore*?

100 Thomas Winning has a top job in which organisation?

101 Which youth organisation was founded in Glasgow by Thurso-born William Smith?

102 Which Nobel Prize-winning scientist discovered the mould from which penicillin was made?

103 Who wrote *The 39 Steps*?

104 Robert Louis Stevenson wrote:

O Leerie, I'll go round at night
And light the lamps with you.

How were four generations of Stevenson's relations responsible for lighting the night?

105 What is the exact date of Robert Burns' birth?

106 . . . and after his death on the 21st July, 1796, where was he buried?

107 Film stars are often associated with roles which they made famous. Which actor is best known as Scrooge?

108 . . . and which one as pompous surgeon Sir Lancelot Spratt in the *Doctor* films?

SECTION 2

MODERN SCOTLAND

GAME 2

109 Every Hogmanay, up to two million TV sets are tuned into the miserable monologues of which minister?

110 In March 1987, how did Scotsman Sylvester McCoy follow in the footsteps of Colin Baker?

111 Which Labour MP wrote the controversial anti-monarchy book *My Queen and I,* published in 1973?

112 Which establishment became the only hotel outside London to win five red stars from the AA in 1986?

113 Which team surprised everybody by winning the final of the English village cricket championship at Lords in 1985?

114 Brewing giants Guinness fought a successful battle against the Argyll Group in 1986, and took over which company?

115 Oil industry links have led to Grampian Region being twinned with which American city?

116 How did the Scots secure English soil in 1977?

117 Two Scots were major protagonists during the prolonged 1985 coal strike. Which one was the National Coal Board chairman?

118 . . . and who was the National Union of Miner's vice-president?

119 Who is the most famous former inmate to have benefited from the Special Unit at Barlinnie Prison?

120 . . . and who spent seven years in jail after being wrongfully convicted of murder, then received a full pardon and £50,000 compensation when released in 1976?

ESTABLISHMENTS

GAME 2

121 Which is Scotland's oldest university?

122 Which is Scotland's best-selling daily paper?

123 Where are the headquarters of Renfrew District Council?

124 The buildings of George Square, Edinburgh have been taken over by which institution?

125 Name any one of the three districts in Fife Region.

126 The Free Church of Scotland is sometimes known by which nickname?

127 Which kind of council is responsible for housing — regional or district?

128 Which Scottish university has the largest number of students?

129 Where is Saughton Prison?

130 . . . and Craiginches Prison?

131 Which evening newspaper is published in Edinburgh?

132 . . . and in Dundee?

SPORT

GAME 2

133 Which Scottish missionary won the 400 metres gold in the 1924 Olympics, and was the hero of the film *Chariots of Fire*?

134 Which Gorbals streetfighter became a world boxing champion, only to return to Glasgow and a short life of alcoholism and poverty?

135 Which football team won the first three Scottish Cup Finals?

136 In curling, where is the "house"?

137 Tommy Walker began his soccer career in 1932, two years after the death of Bobby Walker. For which club did both these famous forwards play?

138 Which musclebound Olympic champion enrolled in a Charles Atlas bodybuilding course as a boy?

139 Rangers striker Colin Stein scored a dramatic equaliser against Celtic in the dying seconds of the New Year's Day game, 1971, but what happened next?

140 Which golfer was born in Shrewsbury, Shropshire?

141 Which town has a football ground called Love Street?

142 . . . and which ground is known fondly as "Paradise"?

143 Which type of car did Jim Clark drive throughout his entire formula one career?

144 . . . and in how many grand prix did Jackie Stewart compete during his formula one career?

SECTION 5

THE HIGHLANDS & ISLANDS

GAME 2

145 Where is the prehistoric stone circle of Callanish?

146 Which town has its airport at Dalcross?

147 Which New Zealand city is called by the original Gaelic name for Edinburgh?

148 Which place has won the city section of the Scotland in Bloom scheme ever since it started in 1968?

149 The Red Deer Commission is devoted to the conservation and control of red and sika deer. Where are its headquarters?

150 What is the final destination of trains that start at Inverness and stop at Achanalt, Achnasheen and Achnashellach?

151 *Had you seen these roads before they were made,*
You would lift up your hands and bless . . ., who?

152 Why has the west coast island of Gruinard been off-limits to humans since 1942?

153 Which grain is malted solely to make malt whisky?

154 . . . and which two vegetables are used to make clapshot?

155 What is the more common name for the bird sometimes called the "fishhawk"?

156 . . . and to which loch have thousands of visitors travelled, in order to see these birds since they returned to Scotland in the 1950s?

SECTION 6

HISTORY

GAME 2

157 From which castle did Mary Queen of Scots escape by boat in 1568?

158 The building of the Great Michael in the 16th century was said to have wasted all the woods in Fife except the Royal Forest at Falkland. What was the Great Michael?

159 What Latin derived nickname was used to describe the natives of Scotland during the Roman occupation?

160 Which important deal was struck only after England agreed to pay £398,085 and 10 shillings?

161 The standard 19th-century Royal Navy gun was named after its place of manufacture, the Carron Iron Works near Falkirk. What was it called?

162 Name the earthwork rampart which the Romans constructed between the rivers Forth and Clyde?

163 The building of steelworks in 1934 attracted thousands of Scots to a Northamptonshire town, earning it the nickname "Little Scotland". Which town?

164 Which idealistic millowner created the model village of New Lanark during the Industrial Revolution?

165 Who founded the first religious settlement on the island of Iona in the 6th Century?

166 . . . and who founded the modern religious settlement known as the Iona Community in 1938?

167 Generations of MacCrimmons served as musicians to the Clan MacLeod on which instrument?

168 . . . and another of the MacLeod chief's musicians in the 17th Century was Daal Morrison, a legendary player on which instrument?

SECTION 7

FROM A' THE AIRTS

GAME 2

169 Neil Munro's best-known novel, inspired one of BBC Scotland's most famous comedy series. What was the name of both novel and series?

170 The song *Donald whaur's yer troosers?* is associated with which entertainer?

171 By what name is novelist James Leslie Mitchell better known?

172 Which singer failed to prevent the screening of an unflattering documentary about him in 1985?

173 Which famous novel, set in a girl's school, was written by Muriel Spark?

174 Who began her showbusiness career as the token female on the Larry Grayson TV show *The Generation Game* in the 1970s?

175 In which village is the shop kept by Isabel Blair?

176 The Perthshire town of Callander was the setting for which popular 1960s TV series?

177 Which instrument is played by Scottish country danceband leader Jim McLeod?

178 . . . and by Bobby Macleod?

179 Give the next line in this quotation from Robert Burns

O wad some power the giftie gie' us . . . .

180 . . . and the next line in this one

Scots, wha hae wi' Wallace bled . . . .

SECTION 8

THE LOWLANDS

GAME 2

181 In which town is the modern shopping centre complex called The Briggait?

182 Which is the highest mountain in southern Scotland?

183 Perthshire has two luxurious hotels known as hydros. State where either of them is situated.

184 Which town has railway stations called High and Grahamston?

185 What kind of person is a "gapus"?

186 Why did the name of a Fife town terrify generations of Scottish schoolchildren?

187 Where are the People's Palace and Pollok House?

188 Twenty men take four years to complete which job?

189 According to Robert Burns, which place . . . "Ne'er a town surpasses, For honest men, and bonny lasses"?

190 . . . and which place is known as the "Honest Town"?

191 Which city was labelled "No Mean City" in the 1930s?

192 . . . and which city has been described as "the heroin and AIDS capital of Europe"?

GAME 2
ANSWERS

·GREAT SCOT!·

97 Lulu (in 1948).
98 The watt (after James Watt).
99 Sir Compton Mackenzie.
100 The Catholic Church (he is Archbishop of Glasgow).
101 The Boy's Brigade.
102 Sir Alexander Fleming.
103 John Buchan.
104 They designed many of Scotland's lighthouses.
105 January 25th, 1759.
106 St Michael's Kirkyard, Dumfries.
107 Alastair Sim (who played the part in the 1951 film, *Scrooge*).
108 James Robertson Justice.

·MODERN SCOTLAND·

109 The Rev IM Jolly (created by Rikki Fulton in the *Scotch and Wry* show).
110 By becoming the BBC's new (and seventh) *Doctor Who.*
111 Willie Hamilton (MP for Fife Central).
112 Gleneagles Hotel (in Perthshire).
113 Freuchie (from Fife, they beat Rowledge).
114 The Distillers Company plc.
115 Houston, Texas.
116 Scottish football fans invaded the pitch at Wembley, cutting patches of turf as souvenirs and bringing down the goalposts (Scotland had just beaten England, 2-1).
117 Ian MacGregor.
118 Mick McGahey.
119 Jimmy Boyle.
120 Paddy Meehan.

GAME 2 ANSWERS

·ESTABLISHMENTS·

121 St Andrews (1411).
122 *The Daily Record.*
123 Paisley.
124 Edinburgh University.
125 Dunfermline, Kirkcaldy, or North East Fife.
126 The "wee frees".
127 District.
128 Glasgow.
129 Edinburgh.
130 Aberdeen.
131 *The Evening News.*
132 *The Evening Telegraph.*

·SPORT·

133 Eric Liddell (who refused to compete in the 100 metre heats because they were held on the Sabbath).
134 Benny Lynch (who died, friendless, in 1946).
135 Queen's Park (1874-6).
136 It is the circle to which the players curl their stones.
137 Hearts.
138 Allan Wells.
139 The Ibrox Disaster (in which 66 people were crushed to death when departing fans tried to return up Staircase 13 after Stein had scored).
140 Sandy Lyle.
141 Paisley (home of St Mirren).
142 Parkhead (also known as Celtic Park).
143 A Lotus (powered by Coventry-Climax, BRM and Ford engines).
144 Ninety-nine, of which he won 27.

GAME 2
ANSWERS

·THE HIGHLANDS & ISLANDS·

145 The Isle of Lewis.
146 Inverness.
147 Dunedin (Dun Eidean, meaning "The fortress of Edin").
148 Aberdeen.
149 Inverness.
150 Kyle of Lochalsh.
151 . . . General Wade (who built 250 miles of military roads and 28 bridges after the Jacobite uprising of 1715).
152 Because germ warfare experiments contaminated the island with anthrax spores.
153 Barley.
154 Potatoes and turnip.
155 The osprey.
156 Loch Garten (near Aviemore).

·HISTORY·

157 Loch Leven Castle.
158 A ship (the largest in Britain at that time).
159 The Picts (in Latin, Picti).
160 The Union of Parliaments of England and Scotland (the money paid off Scotland's national debt).
161 The carronade.
162 The Antonine Wall.
163 Corby.
164 Robert Owen.
165 St Columba (in AD 563).
166 Lord MacLeod of Fuinary (when he was the Rev. George MacLeod).
167 The bagpipes.
168 The harp.

GAME 2 ANSWERS

·FROM A' THE AIRTS·

169 *The Vital Spark.*
170 Andy Stewart.
171 Lewis Grassic Gibbon.
172 Calum Kennedy. (The programme, about a trouble-torn Highland tour, was called *Calum Kennedy's Commando Course.)*
173 *The Prime of Miss Jean Brodie.*
174 Isla St Clair.
175 Glendarroch (fictional setting of the STV soap opera *Take The High Road*).
176 *Dr Finlay's Casebook.*
177 Piano.
178 Accordion.
179 *To see oorsels as ithers see us.*
180 *Scots wham Bruce has often led.*

·THE LOWLANDS·

181 Glasgow.
182 The Merrick, in Galloway, 2766′ (843m).
183 Crieff and Dunblane.
184 Falkirk.
185 A fool.
186 The "Lochgelly" was a strap named after the town where it was made.
187 Glasgow.
188 Painting the Forth Rail Bridge (which has 145 acres of steelwork).
189 Ayr.
190 Musselburgh.
191 Glasgow (the title of a famous book by Alexander McArthur).
192 Edinburgh.

GREAT SCOT!

GAME 3

193 Singer Kenneth McKellar and film star Tom Conti come from which town?

194 Sir Walter Scott transformed Cartley Hole into what?

195 Which MP turned the sinking of the General Belgrano during the Falklands War into a personal campaign against the government?

196 Which poet went to see Queen Victoria at Balmoral, only to be turned back at the gate?

197 Which broadcaster, brought up in Edinburgh, is the son of the former Icelandic consul-general in Scotland?

198 Which actor played the monk William of Baskerville in the 1986 film, *The Name of the Rose*?

199 Which impressionist was a guest on the first programme of the TV chat-show *Wogan*?

200 Which author not only created a famous detective character, but actually advised the police on solving crimes?

201 Which comedian is associated with the phrase "Sausages is the boy"?

202 . . . and which is associated with the phrase "Parliamo Glasgow"?

203 Which Fife weaver's son became one of the world's richest steelmen?

204 . . . and which industry provided a fortune for tycoon William Burrell?

SECTION 2

MODERN SCOTLAND

GAME 3

205 Which was Scotland's first independent radio station?

206 Which Euro-MP is known as "Madame Ecosse"?

207 Why might a large hole in the ground behind Edinburgh's Usher Hall inspire an opera?

208 Where was a nuclear power station built east of Edinburgh in the 1980s?

209 Plans to hold the 1985 National Mod overseas, for the first time, were eventually scrapped. In which country would it have been held?

210 Which former government minister, raised in Scotland, died in 1986 at the age of 101?

211 Which arts jamboree started off with less than ten productions in 1947, but featured more than 900 different shows in 1986?

212 Which Tory MP, later to become Secretary of State for Scotland, was a supporter of a Scottish Assembly before the 1979 devolution referendum?

213 Who scored the goal that took Scotland to the 1986 World Cup Finals in Mexico?

214 . . . and who scored Scotland's only goal in Mexico?

215 Where is Europe's largest oil terminal?

216 . . . and where is Europe's largest white fish port?

ESTABLISHMENTS

GAME 3

217 Which Scot appears on the Bank of Scotland's £1, £5 and £10 notes?

218 Who is the only British subject allowed to maintain a private army, and what is it called?

219 During the General Assembly, which Edinburgh building becomes official residence of the Queen's Lord High Commissioner?

220 Which regional council have their headquarters at Newtown St Boswells?

221 What started in Aberdeen with horse-racing from Catterick, back in 1961?

222 The Fraser of Allander Institute is a Scottish economic research organisation. Who is the famous son of Lord Fraser of Allander?

223 Dunfermline College of Physical Education is not in Dunfermline. Where is it?

224 Prince Andrew is the Duke of York. Who is the Duke of Rothesay?

225 Which army regiment recruit from the Highland Region?

226 . . . and which from most of Grampian Region?

227 Which castle is the ancestral home of Queen Elizabeth the Queen Mother?

228 . . . and which castle is her summer home?

SPORT

GAME 3

229 Who took over as captain of Scotland's rugby team in 1986?

230 How many goals did Arbroath score against Bon Accord in the record-breaking soccer victory of 1885?

231 Which was the fourth skiing centre opened in Scotland, close to Tomintoul?

232 Which Spurs player did Rangers sign in early 1987?

233 What happens at a bonspiel?

234 On which canal do the Honourable Society of Edinburgh Boaters hold their punting competitions?

235 In 1987, which rugby club won the Scottish Division One championship for the tenth time in 14 years?

236 Hampden Park is the home ground of which football club?

237 Name the ruling body in charge of Scottish cricket?

238 . . . and name the authority which organises curling championships in Scotland?

239 Which organisation has its address at 6 Park Gardens, Glasgow?

240 . . . and which is the governing body for rules of golf throughout the world (except for North America)?

SECTION 5

THE HIGHLANDS & ISLANDS

GAME 3

241 Drumochter Pass and Slochd Summit are two of the bleakest stretches on which road?

242 Where is the Clan Donald centre?

243 Partan Bree is a kind of soup, but what does the Gaelic word "partan" mean?

244 Place these islands in order, from south to north: Harris, North Uist, Barra.

245 Where is the Fairy Flag kept?

246 Which Gaelic singer used the name "Aneka", and singing in English, reached number one with the song *Japanese Boy* in 1981?

247 Which game bird became extinct in Britain 200 years ago but is now widespread in the Highlands after reintroduction from Sweden in the 1830s?

248 Which group of islands is home to the largest colony of gannets in Britain?

249 Where is the Old Man of Hoy?

250 . . . and MacLeod's Maidens?

251 Just like Land's End, John O'Groats is not really one of Britain's most extreme points. What is the farthest point north in Scotland?

252 . . . and the farthest point west?

SECTION 6

HISTORY

GAME 3

253 How many times did James VI return to Scotland after leaving to become the first sovereign of the British Isles?

254 Which King died at Flodden?

255 Who won at Philiphaugh near Selkirk in 1645, when the Marquis of Montrose led Highland clansmen and Irish Catholics against anti-Catholic Covenanters?

256 The worst accident of its kind happened at Quintinshill near Gretna in 1915. What was it?

257 Name the notorious American organisation set up by men of Scots descent as a vigilante group to protect farmers after the American Civil War?

258 What did Edinburgh woman Jenny Geddes supposedly do after screaming at Dean Hanna: "Dost thou dare to say mass in my lug?"?

259 In the early decades of this century, the Argyll and Arrol-Johnston firms were two of Scotland's leading makers of what?

260 What was the proper title held by the man Highlanders called "The Butcher"?

261 The Scots first appear in the historical records in about AD 400. Where had they come from?

262 . . . and what language did they speak?

263 Which deposed monarch was executed by the English in 1587?

264 . . . and what did the English then do to that monarch's son in 1603?

SECTION 7

FROM A' THE AIRTS

GAME 3

265 Which famous former folksinger described folk music as "Four woolly pullovers singing *The Wild Rover*"?

266 Who had a hit single with *Modern Girl* in 1980?

267 What is the name given to the classical style of bagpipe music?

268 Which Edinburgh actor played the unlikely headmistress in the film *The Belles of St Trinians*?

269 Which actor is well known for his portrayals of Robert Burns?

270 In which successful 1967 film did Lulu make her film debut?

271 The TV series *Dr Finlay's Casebook* made Bill Simpson and Andrew Cruickshank weel-kent faces, but which community did they serve?

272 *Her faither's jist a waster,*
Her mither's on the game . . . .

Who is the heroine of this popular song?

273 According to Robert Burns, what is "chief of Scotia's food"?

274 . . . and what is "the hell o' a' diseases"?

275 Which entertainer is chiefly associated with the TV series *The White Heather Show*?

276 . . . and who is associated with the radio series *Take the Floor*?

SECTION 8

THE LOWLANDS

GAME 3

277 What opened in Glasgow in 1896, closed in 1977 and then reopened in 1980?

278 At what time of the day is Mons Meg fired at Edinburgh Castle?

279 Why is it dangerous to get out of a car at Blair Drummond?

280 Just as Edinburgh's Nor' Loch was drained to make way for Princes Street Gardens, so the city's old Burgh Loch was drained to be replaced by what?

281 Where are Claypotts Castle and Camperdown Park?

282 Sir William Wallace and Sir Walter Scott are both commemorated by large monuments. Where are they?

283 Place these towns in order, west to east: Port Glasgow, Gourock, Greenock?

284 Quaint Scottish placenames like Auchtermuchty are not confined to the countryside. Around which city are the areas of Auchenshuggle and Carnwadric?

285 In which city is the Advocates' Library?

286 . . . and in which city is the Mitchell Library?

287 Certain common Christian names have slang equivalents. Who is "Shuggie"?

288 . . . and who is "Dod"?

GAME 3 ANSWERS

·GREAT SCOT!·

193 Paisley.
194 Abbotsford House (Cartley Hole was the farm which he transformed into a baronial mansion).
195 Tam Dalyell (MP for Linlithgow).
196 William McGonagall (in 1878).
197 Magnus Magnusson.
198 Sean Connery.
199 Rory Bremner (in 1985).
200 Sir Arthur Conan Doyle.
201 Jimmy Logan.
202 Stanley Baxter.
203 Andrew Carnegie (who made his fortune in America).
204 Shipping.

·MODERN SCOTLAND·

205 Radio Clyde (began transmissions in 1973).
206 Winnie Ewing.
207 Because the "hole in the ground" has for decades been earmarked as the site for the city's opera house, which has yet to be built.
208 Torness.
209 Canada (in Cape Breton).
210 Manny Shinwell.
211 The Fringe.
212 Malcolm Rifkind (MP for Edinburgh Pentlands).
213 Frank MacAvennie (against Australia).
214 Gordon Strachan (against West Germany).
215 Sullom Voe (in the Shetlands).
216 Peterhead.

GAME 3 ANSWERS

·ESTABLISHMENTS·

217 Sir Walter Scott.
218 The Duke of Atholl and the Atholl Highlanders.
219 The Palace of Holyroodhouse.
220 Borders Region.
221 Grampian Television.
222 Sir Hugh Fraser.
223 Edinburgh.
224 Prince Charles.
225 The Queen's Own Highlanders.
226 The Gordon Highlanders.
227 Glamis Castle (in Angus).
228 Castle of Mey (in Caithness).

·SPORT·

229 Colin Deans.
230 36 (the score was 36-0).
231 The Lecht.
232 Graham Roberts.
233 A curling match (a bonspiel usually occurs outdoors).
234 The Union Canal.
235 Hawick.
236 Queen's Park.
237 Scottish Cricket Union.
238 Royal Caledonian Curling Club.
239 The Scottish Football Association.
240 The Royal and Ancient Golf Club (St Andrews).

GAME 3 ANSWERS

·THE HIGHLANDS & ISLANDS·

241 The A9.
242 The Isle of Skye.
243 A crab.
244 Barra, North Uist, Harris.
245 Dunvegan Castle (on the Isle of Skye).
246 Mary Sandeman.
247 The capercaillie.
248 St Kilda.
249 The Orkney Isles (a rock pinnacle on the Isle of Hoy).
250 Skye (a group of pinnacles at the entrance to Loch Bracadale).
251 Dunnet Head.
252 Ardnamurchan Point (in Argyll).

·HISTORY·

253 Once.
254 James IV (in 1513).
255 The Covenanters.
256 A railway accident in which 227 people died (when a troop train steamed head-on into a local train, and many survivors were then mowed down by the Euston-Glasgow express train).
257 The Klu Klux Klan.
258 She threw her stool at him (this happened in St Giles Cathedral in 1637, as a Presbyterean protest against Charles I's prayer book).
259 Motor cars.
260 The Duke of Cumberland (who ordered the butchering of Jacobites, wounded or captured, at Culloden).
261 Ireland.
262 Gaelic.
263 Mary Queen of Scots.
264 They made him their king (he was James VI of Scotland, and I of Britain).

GAME 3
ANSWERS

·FROM A' THE AIRTS·

265 Billy Connolly.
266 Sheena Easton.
267 The pibroch (perhaps the ultimate test of a piper's ability).
268 Alastair Sim.
269 John Cairney.
270 *To Sir With Love* (starring Sidney Poitier).
271 Tannochbrae.
272 *The Kelty Clippie* (from the song of that name, by Fifer John Watt).
273 Haggis (in *The Cottar's Saturday Night*).
274 Toothache (in *Address to the Toothache*).
275 Andy Stewart (the compere from 1960 onwards).
276 Robbie Shepherd.

·THE LOWLANDS·

277 The underground rail network.
278 One pm.
279 Because this is where Scotland's first safari park was located.
280 The Meadows.
281 Dundee.
282 The Wallace Monument is near Stirling, and the Scott monument is in Princes St, Edinburgh.
283 Gourock, Greenock, Port Glasgow.
284 Glasgow.
285 Edinburgh.
286 Glasgow.
287 Hugh.
288 George.

GREAT SCOT!

GAME 4

289 What is the common name for Collum-Cille?

290 Who is the only Scot to have won the Eurovision Song Contest, in 1969?

291 Which musical instrument is associated with Neil Gow?

292 Which Glasgow star had number one hits in 1957 with *Cumberland Gap* and *Gambling Man*?

293 *A Drunk Man Looks at the Thistle* was the most famous work by which poet?

294 What major role did Brechin-born inventor Sir Robert Watson-Watt play in the defeat of Hitler?

295 Who earned fame as the friend and biographer of 18th-century English writer Dr Samuel Johnson?

296 Which 18th-century native of Kirkcaldy is widely regarded as the founder of classical economics?

297 Who was the only Scotsman to be a Liberal prime-minister in the 20th Century?

298 . . . and who was Britain's first Labour prime minister?

299 Who resigned as Director-General of the BBC in January 1987?

300 . . . and who took over as head of STV in 1986?

MODERN SCOTLAND

GAME 4

301 How did corned beef cut off thousands of Scots in 1964?

302 Which 1960s pop star had a band called the Luvvers?

303 Who has excelled his father, a Campbeltown grocer, by developing the supermarket chains of Fine Fare, Presto and Safeway?

304 The spectacular Eden Court Theatre building was opened in 1976. Where is it?

305 Who masterminded the rise of the Bay City Rollers pop group in the 1970s?

306 Which Lewisman became a popular presenter of the BBC magazine programme *Pebble Mill at One*, before dying of a heart attack in 1984?

307 Which army regiment was formed in 1961 by the amalgamation of the Queen's Own Cameron Highlanders and the Seaforth Highlanders?

308 Edinburgh staged the Commonwealth Games in 1986, but in which previous year were the games held there?

309 The fragile economy of the Highlands was dealt a double blow in the early 1980s with the closure of two major industrial plants. Which community lost its aluminium smelter?

310 . . . and which lost its paper pulp mill?

311 Which 1986 film centred around a sequence of miraculous events at a Catholic school in Glasgow?

312 . . . and which one dealt with a war between ice cream van operators in Glasgow?

SECTION 3

ESTABLISHMENTS

GAME 4

313 Which biblical symbol is the emblem of the Church of Scotland?

314 Who is the Liberal Party's longest-serving Scottish MP?

315 How many districts are there in Grampian Region?

316 The court verdict in both Scotland and England can be "guilty" or "not guilty", but what is the "third verdict" which exists only in Scotland?

317 Marischal College is part of which university?

318 Which annual event has been called "the Whisky Olympics"?

319 Which police force covers two separate regions?

320 The Episcopal cathedrals of Inverness and Aberdeen share the same name. What is it?

321 Before local government reorganisation, which was Scotland's smallest county?

322 . . . and after reorganisation, which was Scotland's smallest region?

323 Where is Jordanhill College of Education?

324 . . . and Duncan of Jordanstone College of Art?

SECTION 4

SPORT

GAME 4

325 Where was the game of Rugby Sevens invented?

326 The Scottish Sports Council have two national training centres at which town?

327 Which football club is nicknamed the "Loons"?

328 If Rangers and Celtic are the Old Firm of football, who are the Old Firm of shinty?

329 Which famous football club was set up in 1888 in order to raise money to buy food and clothing for the poor?

330 Which two athletes named Ian set Meadowbank alight by finishing first and second in the 1970 Commonwealth Games 5000 metres final?

331 Which senior football club were formerly called Ferranti Thistle?

332 The future captains of Scotland's Rugby team and England's Cricket team once played alongside each other in an Ayr Academy First XV. Name either of them.

333 Which sport is known as "the roaring game"?

334 . . . and which was called "Scotch Croquet" by overseas detractors in the 1890s?

335 Asia has given us some of our greatest sportsmen — name the swimmer born in Sri Lanka.

336 . . . and the runner born in China.

THE HIGHLANDS & ISLANDS

GAME 4

337 Which game bird turns white in winter?

338 What is Neptune's Staircase?

339 The Gaelic-derived word "clachan" means what in English?

340 What is unusual about the interior of Ben Cruachan near Oban?

341 Where was the coldest-ever temperature twice recorded in Britain?

342 The ferry from Wemyss Bay serves which island?

343 Loch Ness, Scotland's deepest loch, is seawater. Which is the deepest freshwater loch?

344 What is the popular name for the spectacular railway line which crosses Rannoch Moor and the Glenfinnan Viaduct?

345 How do the young men of Kirkwall, in Orkney, celebrate Christmas and New Year's Day?

346 . . . and what is the name given to the Viking fire festivals held throughout the Shetland Isles in the New Year?

347 The West Highlands have two groups of mountains called "Sisters". How many Sisters are there in Kintail, near Kyle of Lochalsh?

348 . . . and how many in Glencoe?

SECTION 6

HISTORY

GAME 4

349 In which church was John Knox the minister in the years immediately before his death in 1572?

350 In which castle was Mary Queen of Scots beheaded?

351 What was known as "Cleanse the Causeway"?

352 Name the famous Aberdeenshire demonstration against the National Insurance Act of 1911.

353 Where did the Battle of the Braes take place?

354

The floo'ers o' the forest fought aye the foremost,
The pride o' our land now lie caved in the clay.

Where exactly was the clay referred to by the Balladeer where up to 10,000 Scottish fighters lay dead?

355 Which French town has a street called Avenue of the 51st Highland Division, and why?

356 James Craig wrote this of his finest creation:

August, around, what PUBLIC WORKS I see!
Lo, stately streets! lo, squares that court the breeze!

What was he referring to?

357 Which language was used for the Declaration of Arbroath in 1320?

358 . . . and which language was used during John Knox's bitter audiences with Mary Queen of Scots?

359 Which politician won Glasgow Hillhead in the 1980s?

360 . . . and which Englishman lost his Dundee seat in the 1920s?

FROM A' THE AIRTS

GAME 4

361 How is the name of the 13th-century scholar John Duns Scotus preserved in the English language today?

362 Who wrote the novel *The Silver Darlings*?

363 Which second-generation Italian played Pope Leo XIV in the 1986 film *Saving Grace*?

364 In what field has Leith man Dick Gaughan found international acclaim recently?

365 What was the name of the horse which lost its tail in *Tam O'Shanter*?

366 What are the first names of the Alexander Brothers musical duo?

367 How did the 7:84 theatre company get their name?

368 The brilliant investigative techniques of which famous fictional character were based on the medical methods of Dr Joseph Bell of Edinburgh?

369 In the John Buchan thriller *The 39 Steps,* which character, suspected of murder, is pursued across Scotland?

370 . . . and who played this role in the best-known film version of 1935?

371 TV star Iain Cuthbertson introduced which peculiarly Scottish institution to viewers south of the border when he played the title role in the TV series *Sutherland's Law*?

372 . . . and he also played a distinctly suspicious character, called Charlie Endell, in which comedy series?

THE LOWLANDS

GAME 4

373 What is "Paddy's Milestone" otherwise known as?

374 In which city is the bleak council-housing area of Niddrie?

375 What are the Corra Linn and the Grey Mare's Tail?

376 Which Fife fishing town is sometimes called Ainster?

377 Which place was Robert Louis Stevenson describing when he wrote: "The weather is . . . a downright meteorological purgatory in the spring. The delicate die early"?

378 Where is the concert venue called the Caird Hall?

379 Where were "nicky tams" worn?

380 In which castle is St Margaret's Chapel?

381 In the Scots tongue, what kind of garment is a *gansey*?

382 . . . and a *sark*?

383 Which Perthshire town is known as "The Lang Toun"?

384 . . . and which Fife town is also called the same name?

·GREAT SCOT!·

289 St Columba.
290 Lulu (1st equal with *Boom-Bang-a-Bang*).
291 The fiddle (or violin: he was the Duke of Atholl's celebrated fiddler and composer in the 18th century).
292 Lonnie Donegan.
293 Hugh MacDiarmid (real name Christopher Grieve).
294 He invented the radar.
295 James Boswell.
296 Adam Smith.
297 Sir Henry Campbell-Bannerman.
298 James Ramsay MacDonald.
299 Alasdair Milne.
300 Gus Macdonald.

·MODERN SCOTLAND·

301 Because Aberdeen became quarantined by an outbreak of typhoid from infected corned beef.
302 Lulu.
303 James Gulliver.
304 Inverness.
305 Tam Paton.
306 Donny MacLeod.
307 The Queen's Own Highlanders.
308 1970.
309 Invergordon.
310 Corpach, near Fort William.
311 *Heavenly Pursuits.*
312 *Comfort and Joy* (1984).

GAME 4
ANSWERS

·ESTABLISHMENTS·

313 The burning bush.
314 Russell Johnston (MP for Inverness, Nairn and Lochaber).
315 Five (Aberdeen; Banff & Buchan; Gordon; Kincardine & Deeside; Moray).
316 "Not proven".
317 Aberdeen.
318 The National Mod (the major Gaelic Festival).
319 Lothian and Borders Police Force.
320 St Andrew's.
321 Clackmannanshire.
322 Fife.
323 Glasgow.
324 Dundee.

·SPORT·

325 Melrose.
326 Largs (the Inverclyde Centre, and for water sports, the Cumbrae Centre).
327 Forfar Athletic.
328 Kingussie and Newtonmore.
329 Celtic.
330 Ian Stewart (1st) and Ian McCafferty (2nd).
331 Meadowbank Thistle.
332 Ian McLauchlan (rugby) and Mike Denness (cricket).
333 Curling.
334 Golf.
335 David Wilkie.
336 Eric Liddell.

GAME 4
ANSWERS

·THE HIGHLANDS & ISLANDS·

337 The ptarmigan.
338 A series of eight locks in the Caledonian Canal at Banavie.
339 A small village.
340 It contains a hydro-electric power station.
341 Braemar (–27°C was recorded in 1895 and 1982).
342 Bute.
343 Loch Morar (near Mallaig).
344 The West Highland Line.
345 By playing the Ba' game (a mob football game).
346 Up-Helly-Aa (which involves the burning of a Viking longship).
347 Five.
348 Three.

·HISTORY·

349 St Giles, Edinburgh.
350 Fotheringay Castle, 1587.
351 A bloody Edinburgh brawl between the powerful Hamilton and Douglas factions in 1520.
352 The Turra Coo incident (the "Turriff cow" in question was owned by the farmer who led the protest).
353 The Isle of Skye (the last battle fought on British soil which forced Gladstone to set up a Royal Commission to look into crofters' grievances).
354 At Flodden, 1513.
355 St Valery-en-Caux (where the division surrendered in 1940, but returned as liberators in 1944 and are commemorated in the street's name).
356 Edinburgh's New Town (based on Craig's 1767 designs).
357 Latin.
358 French.
359 Roy Jenkins.
360 Winston Churchill.

GAME 4
ANSWERS

·FROM A' THE AIRTS·

361 By the word "dunce".
362 Neil Gunn (1941).
363 Tom Conti.
364 Folk music.
365 "Maggie" or "Meg".
366 Tom and Jack.
367 From the statistic that 7% of the country's population own 84% of the wealth.
368 Sherlock Holmes.
369 Richard Hannay.
370 Robert Donat.
371 The office of procurator fiscal.
372 *Budgie* (also starring Adam Faith and Russell Hunter).

·THE LOWLANDS·

373 Ailsa Craig (a granite mass, 10 miles off the Ayrshire coast).
374 Edinburgh.
375 Waterfalls (near Lanark and Moffat respectively).
376 Anstruther.
377 Edinburgh (his native town).
378 Dundee.
379 On the leg (a string worn below the knee by farm labourers toiling in the mud).
380 Edinburgh Castle.
381 A jersey.
382 A shirt.
383 Auchterarder.
384 Kirkcaldy.

GREAT SCOT!

385 How did John Napier's bones live on, centuries after his death?

386 Who was the "Strathspey King"?

387 Which duty was shared by Robert Burns in the 18th Century and Neil Gunn in the 20th?

388 Who addresses Princess Alexandra as "sweetie" in public?

389 Which writer and lawyer was also Sheriff of Selkirkshire?

390 Which comedian received the highest fee ever for a role played in a silent film?

391 Who played the doom-laden Private Fraser in the TV series *Dad's Army*?

392 What are the full names of the duo whose song *Flower of Scotland* is among the best-known in the country?

393 Which actor played the lead role in the 1984 film *Comfort and Joy*?

394 . . . and in the 1986 film *Heavenly Pursuits*?

395 Great Scots were in the vanguard of British socialism in its early years. Which Scot founded the Independent Labour Party?

396 . . . and which Scot, the first Soviet consul in Britain, had a street named after him in Leningrad?

SECTION 2

MODERN SCOTLAND

GAME 5

397 Name Glasgow's major arts festival, launched in 1983?

398 Where was Scotland's first butterfly farm opened, in 1985?

399 Name the manager of the Scottish World Cup Squad in 1974?

400 Who led the Argyll and Sutherland Highlanders when they stormed the terrorist-held town of Crater, in Aden in 1967?

401 Graeme Sounness' arrival at Ibrox in 1986 was allegedly plotted in Paris by three men linked to which building group?

402 Which exhibition organiser for the National Museum of Antiquities burst on to the pop scene as a presenter of the TV show *The Tube*?

403 In which year were both local government and senior football reorganised in Scotland?

404 In 1969, after becoming the first Briton to win the British Open for 18 years, golfer Tony Jacklin triumphantly hurled the ball into the crowd. Which little lad almost caught it?

405 In which New Town did director Bill Forsyth film *Gregory's Girl*?

406 . . . and in which picturesque North-east village was *Local Hero* partly shot?

407 Where was Scotland's first official Country park opened in 1970?

408 . . . and which was Scotland's first official long-distance footpath, opened in 1980?

ESTABLISHMENTS

GAME 5

409 What are the Jolly Beggars' Clubs, which exist in several Scottish towns?

410 The Orkney isles are covered by which police force?

411 The exclusive Edinburgh school building of John Watson's College was converted into which national institution in 1984?

412 Name two of the first three nuclear power complexes established in Scotland?

413 The Queen's Hall in Edinburgh is the permanent home of which orchestra?

414 St Salvator's College is part of which University?

415 Aberdeen is to Regensburg and Inverness to Augsburg, as Edinburgh is to which city?

416 The Royal Scottish Museum and the National Museum of Antiquities were merged to form what?

417 Which is the oldest infantry regiment in the British Army?

418 . . . and which is the oldest Highland Regiment?

419 Several major British organisations are based in Scotland. Where are the national headquarters of the Forestry Commission?

420 . . . and of the General Accident Corporation?

SPORT

GAME 5

421 Which skiing centre is run by the White Corries company?

422 Which actor was the narrator on *Gol!*, the official film of the 1982 World Cup finals in Spain?

423 What makes the Celtic football strip unique in Scotland?

424 Winnie Shaw and Joyce Barclay dominated which sport in Scotland in the 1960s and early 1970s?

425 "The Sons meet the Bairns" — what does this mean in football jargon?

426 Which international footballer had to be rescued from a rowing boat off Largs?

427 Who was the skip of the team which won Scotland's only World Curling Championship in 1967?

428 Prior to taking over the national team in 1978, Jock Stein was in charge of his last club for less than two months. Which club was it?

429 Which two Scots played for Manchester United when they became the first English team to win the European Cup in 1968?

430 . . . and who was their manager?

431 How many players are there in a curling team?

432 . . . and how many in a shinty team?

SECTION 5

THE HIGHLANDS & ISLANDS

GAME 5

433 Which Scottish king apparently had a big head?

434 Place these districts in order, from east to west: Moray, Banff & Buchan, Nairn.

435 Which famous English writer made his home on the island of Jura?

436 What is "the long island"?

437 The Kessock Bridge links which two local authority districts?

438 Which normally useless liquid is valued in the Hebrides, and why?

439 Give the meaning of either a "crannog" or a "coronach"?

440 In which islands would you find these reminders of the two world wars — the Kitchener Memorial and the Churchill Barriers?

441 What is the "Hielan'man's Umbrella"?

442 . . . and who were the "Skye Navy"?

443 The gull-like bird called the Fulmar now breeds right around the coastline, but last century it could only be found where?

444 . . . and in the same place, Scotland's last specimen of which now-extinct bird was killed by three frightened and superstitious men in 1840?

HISTORY

GAME 5

445 The mutchkin and chopin were much in use between the 17th and 19th Centuries. What were they?

446 The Border Abbeys of Jedburgh, Kelso and Melrose were all built by which 12th-century king?

447 The nickname given to James VI and I's major creditor, George Heriot the goldsmith, lives on in the name of an Edinburgh pub. What is it?

448 Name two of the three husbands of Mary Queen of Scots?

449 How did James Macpherson deceive much of Europe in the 1760s?

450 Who was the Duke of Sutherland's notorious estate factor who was charged with murder for his part in the Highland clearances?

451 Which clan were supposedly given a magic flag by the fairy folk, to help them out in time of dire trouble?

452 *I saw a dead man win a fight,*
And I think that man was I.

According to the ballad, the man who had this dream was James, Earl of Douglas, but where was the fight?

453 Which party held the majority of Scottish seats in Parliament between 1885 and 1918, excepting a six year period?

454 . . . and which party held the majority between 1955 and 1959?

455 The ancient Britons of Strathclyde spoke in a tongue closely related to which Celtic language in use today?

456 . . . and this also resembles which other language spoken on the Continent?

SECTION 7

FROM A' THE AIRTS

GAME 5

457 How many drones are there in a set of bagpipes?

458 What have *Docherty* and *Laidlaw* got in common?

459 Where is the St Magnus Festival held?

460 Which writer was known as "Tusitala" by the people among whom he lived?

461 What do the film *Gregory's Girl* and the soap opera *Crossroads* have in common?

462 According to the complete title of his poem, where did Burns see a louse?

463 *The Monarch of the Glen,* showing a stag in rugged Highland landscape, was one of the most popular paintings in Victorian Britain. Who painted it?

464 What is the title of the popular Scottish song which starts:

Gin a body, meet a body . . . ?

465 Who is the lead singer of the rock group Big Country?

466 . . . and of Simple Minds?

467 The North-east of Scotland has produced several great showmen. Which comedian invented the community of Inversnecky?

468 . . . and which act invented the village of Auchterturra?

THE LOWLANDS

GAME 5

469 What do Bothwell, Hamilton, Harthill, Kinross and Stirling all have in common?

470 Is Rumbledethumps for eating, playing or wearing?

471 Which city has been built close to the Sidlaw Hills?

472 Loch Lomond is divided between which two local-authority regions?

473 Which canal closely follows the line of the Roman fortification called the Antonine Wall?

474 Which valley was recently flooded to become Edinburgh's newest public water supply?

475 Who uttered these words on the 11th March 1972, as he was made a Freeman of Langholm: "I consider this Langholm to be my home town. I have gained a new home today"?

476 What kind of geographical feature is a haugh?

477 Which leading Scottish Theatre is situated in the Gorbals district of Glasgow?

478 . . . and which ballet was written about this area?

479 Where does the annual Fisherman's Walk procession take place?

480 . . . and where does the Kate Kennedy procession take place?

GAME 5
ANSWERS

·GREAT SCOT!·

385 "Napier's Bones" was the name given to the earliest form of logarithmic tables, invented by Napier in the 17th Century.

386 James Scott Skinner (the fiddler).

387 Customs duty (they were both excisemen).

388 Angus Ogilvy (her husband).

389 Sir Walter Scott.

390 Harry Lauder (who received £10,000 to play the grocer in George Pearson's *Huntingtower* in 1927).

391 John Laurie.

392 Roy Williamson and Ronnie Brown of The Corries.

393 Bill Paterson.

394 Tom Conti.

395 James Keir Hardie.

396 John MacLean (MacLean Street).

·MODERN SCOTLAND·

397 The Mayfest.

398 Edinburgh.

399 Willie Ormond.

400 Lt Col Colin Mitchell (known as "Mad Mitch").

401 The Lawrence Building Group.

402 Muriel Gray.

403 1975.

404 Sandy Lyle.

405 Cumbernauld.

406 Pennan.

407 Culzean (in Ayrshire).

408 The West Highland Way (95 miles from Milngavie to Fort William).

GAME 5 ANSWERS

·ESTABLISHMENTS·

409 Burns Clubs.
410 Northern Constabulary (HQ in Inverness)
411 The Scottish National Gallery of Modern Art.
412 Chapelcross (Dumfriesshire), Dounreay (Caithness).
413 The Scottish Chamber Orchestra.
414 St Andrews.
415 Munich (they are all West German twin towns).
416 The Royal Museum of Scotland (in Edinburgh).
417 The Royal Scots (1535).
418 The Black Watch (1739)
419 Edinburgh.
420 Perth.

·SPORT·

421 Glencoe.
422 Sean Connery.
423 The players' numbers are on their shorts.
424 Tennis.
425 Dumbarton ("the Sons") are playing Falkirk ("the bairns").
426 Jimmy Johnstone (of Celtic, during preparations for the 1974 World Cup Finals).
427 Chuck Hay.
428 Leeds United.
429 Pat Crerand and Dennis Law.
430 Matt Busby.
431 Four.
432 Twelve.

GAME 5
ANSWERS

·THE HIGHLANDS & ISLANDS·

433 Malcolm Canmore (in Gaelic, *ceann mor* means big head).
434 Banff & Buchan, Moray, Nairn.
435 George Orwell (he wrote *1984* there).
436 The Isles of Lewis and Harris (which are actually joined together).
437 Inverness District and Ross and Cromarty District.
438 Urine, as it is used in making tweed, as part of the waulking process.
439 A crannog is an ancient loch dwelling and a coronach is a funeral song.
440 The Orkney Isles.
441 A railway bridge (spanning Argyle Street, under which Highlanders used to meet).
442 The men of the Western Isles who worked Glasgow's Clyde ferries.
443 St Kilda.
444 The Great Auk.

·HISTORY·

445 They were standard units of liquid measure.
446 David I.
447 Jinglin' Geordie.
448 Francis, Dauphin of France (later King Francis I); Lord Darnley; the Earl of Bothwell.
449 By convincing almost everyone that his own epic poems were actually translations of the ancient Gaelic writings of the bard Ossian.
450 Patrick Sellar.
451 The Clan MacLeod (by waving the flag, help would arrive — but only on three occasions).
452 The Battle of Otterburn, also known as Chevy Chase, 1388. ("Dead man" Douglas won the day by telling his men, as he lay dying, to wave his banner and shout his name to trick the enemy).
453 The Liberals.
454 The Conservatives.
455 Welsh.
456 Breton (spoken in Brittany).

GAME 5
ANSWERS

·FROM A' THE AIRTS·

457 Three.
458 They are both novels by William MacIlvanney.
459 The Orkney Isles.
460 Robert Louis Stevenson (in Samoa).
461 The actress Dee Hepburn (who played parts in both).
462 On a lady's bonnet.
463 Sir Edwin Landseer.
464 *Comin' through the rye.*
465 Stuart Adamson.
466 Jim Kerr.
467 Harry Gordon (in the 1920s and 30s).
468 The "Scotland the What?" trio.

·THE LOWLANDS·

469 They are the sites of Scotland's five motorway service stations.
470 For eating (it is a Border's dish made with potatoes).
471 Dundee.
472 Strathclyde and Central.
473 The Forth and Clyde Canal.
474 Megget Water, near St Mary's Loch, Selkirkshire.
475 Neil Armstrong, the first man to set foot on the Moon.
476 A piece of flat ground near a river.
477 The Citizens' Theatre.
478 *Miracle in the Gorbals.*
479 Musselburgh (and the adjoining district of Fisherrow).
480 St Andrews.

GREAT SCOT!

GAME 6

481 Where was Prime Minister James Ramsay MacDonald born and bred?

482 Who sang the theme song of the James Bond movie *For Your Eyes Only*?

483 The children's novel *The Wind in the Willows* made writer Kenneth Grahame famous throughout Britain, but where was he born?

484 Where is poet Hugh MacDiarmid buried?

485 The Caledonian Canal was built by one of the first great civil engineers. Who?

486 Which famous broadcaster, nicknamed "Robbie", died in February 1987?

487 Who did Lady Caroline Lamb describe as: "Mad, bad and dangerous to know"?

488 The little village of Largo in Fife produced two of Scotland's most famous mariners. Who were they?

489 Who is known as "the father of geology"?

490 . . . and "the father of documentary films"?

491 Who wrote of William Wallace: "The story of Wallace poured a Scottish prejudice into my veins, which will boil along there till the floodgates of life shut in eternal rest."?

492 . . . and who wrote in his autobiography: "A flame, as Lord Byron has said, seemed to kindle up my entire frame, along with a strong desire to write poetry."?

MODERN SCOTLAND

GAME 6

493 "Let's not lose our dignity" was the last recorded remark made by which Scot, who died in 1985?

494 Which climber was killed in an avalanche while skiing in the Swiss Alps in 1977?

495 Alasdair Gray's first novel won the 1982 Scottish Book of the Year award. What was it called?

496 Which was Scotland's first producing oilfield?

497 Name the two Scottish boxers who were world lightweight champions during the 1970s?

498 Which disc jockey, disabled by multiple sclerosis, finally gave up his Radio Luxembourg show in 1987?

499 Who said "We don't only build boats on the Clyde, we build men"?

500 An incredible total of 127,000 Scots packed into Hampden Stadium for the 1960 European Cup final, in which Eintracht Frankfurt were hammered 7-3, by which team?

501 Where is the Highland oilrig fabrication yard operated by McDermott's?

502 . . . and where is the oil terminal of Flotta?

503 Which Swedish beauty was pop star Rod Stewart's lover?

504 . . . and which American pop star married Jim Kerr, of Simple Minds?

ESTABLISHMENTS

GAME 6

505 The commonest tune for the 23rd psalm, *Crimond*, gets its name from the village where it was written. Where is Crimond?

506 Which art college was designed by architect Charles Rennie Mackintosh?

507 Who led the breakaway of the Free Church from the 1843 General Assembly?

508 Glenrothes is the capital of Fife region, but which district is it in?

509 St Margaret's girls' school and Robert Gordon's boys' school are both where?

510 What does SSTA stand for?

511 What is the full name of the organisation responsible for lighthouses around Scotland and the Isle of Man?

512 Bishop William Elphinstone is known as the founder of which university?

513 Which title is given to the principal law officer of the Crown in Scotland?

514 . . . and to his senior deputy?

515 Where in Edinburgh is the Scottish Office housed?

516 . . . and what is the Scottish Secretary of State's Edinburgh residence called?

SECTION 4

SPORT

GAME 6

517 Hazards called Jockie and Barry can ruin a round at which golf course?

518 How many football teams called United are there in the Scottish League?

519 Moses McNeill was a founder of which football club?

520 Which golf course staged the first British Open?

521 How did Spurs and Scotland football star John White, called "the ghost of White Hart Lane", meet his end?

522 "Wasps" and "Spiders" are the nicknames of which two football clubs?

523 Which rugby star, playing alongside his brother, broke the Scottish international record of points scored in a game, with 21 in 1986?

524 Which football club was promoted in 1976 and 1977 and then relgated in 1978?

525 Name the 1970s international rugby cap named "Mighty Mouse".

526 . . . and the 1980s cap called "The White Shark"?

527 From which town comes the football club affectionately known as "Wee Rovers"?

528 . . . and "Wee Rangers"?

SECTION 5

THE HIGHLANDS & ISLANDS

GAME 6

529 Rannoch Moor is divided between which three local-authority regions?

530 Fifteen miles up the River Dee from Aberdeen stands a 16th-century castle, and 34 miles farther upriver is the Kirk where the Royal Family worship. What are their very similar names?

531 Name the subtropical Highland garden, created by Osgood Mackenzie, where eucalyptus trees flourish.

532 The Orkneys and Shetlands lie within which shipping forecast area?

533 What is "felis sylvestris" usually known as?

534 Where is the broch, or prehistoric round tower, known as Dun Carloway?

535 A Scottish Mountain higher than 3000 feet is called a Munro, but what is the name for a mountain between 2500 and 3000 feet high?

536 Which millionaire hoped to launch an industrial revolution in the Isles of Lewis and Harris by building railways and factories?

537 Which is the largest native land mammal in Great Britain?

538 . . . and the largest bird of prey?

539 On which island is Brodick Castle?

540 . . . and on which island is Kisimul Castle?

SECTION 6

HISTORY

GAME 6

541 Bonny Prince Charlie's invading army got as far as which English town before turning for home again?

542 Which Scot led pioneering expeditions across Canada to the Artic and Pacific Oceans, and is remembered in the name of one of the world's greatest rivers?

543 Which battle, in 1263, was followed by the transfer of the Hebrides and the Isle of Man, from Norway to Scotland?

544 Which famous monastic community in North-east England was founded by missionaries from Iona in AD635?

545 What was the Disclothing Act of 1747?

546 Who urged Queen Elizabeth I to "apply the axe to the root of the evil", and to what was he referring?

547 The execution of smuggler Wilson in 1736 led to which notorious incident in the history of Edinburgh?

548 What is the missing word in this excerpt from the Declaration of Arbroath in 1320: "It is in truth not for glory, nor riches, nor honours that we are fighting, but for . . ."?

549 Who commanded the Scottish army which defeated the English at Stirling Bridge in 1297?

550 . . . and who led the Scottish army destroyed by the English at Flodden in 1513?

551 For which cause, Catholic or Protestant, did the martyr George Wishart die?

552 . . . and for which did the original Cameronians die?

FROM A' THE AIRTS

GAME 6

553 Which pop star once signed up for Brentford football club?

554 Which contemporary poet, born in Motherwell, has plays about Dracula and Frankenstein to her credit?

555 Sandy Bell's pub in Edinburgh has become closely associated with which kind of entertainment?

556 Peter Darrell is the founder of which national arts company?

557 In Shakespeare's play *Macbeth,* where exactly was Macbeth crowned King after he had murdered Duncan?

558 What do the novels *Weir of Hermiston,* by Robert Louis Stevenson, and *The Speak of the Mearns,* by Lewis Grassic Gibbon, have in common?

559 Where is the Garrison Theatre?

560 Who assembled one of the world's largest collections of folksongs during travels around Aberdeenshire with the Rev. James B. Duncan?

561 Who is the well-known father of actress Maureen Beattie?

562 . . . and the well-known son of comedian Jack Short?

563 Complete this folk song chorus:

An ye had been whaur I hae been,
Ye wadne be sae canty-o,
An ye had seen what I hae seen . . . .

564 . . . and what does the word "canty" mean in the chorus?

THE LOWLANDS

GAME 6

565 The fifie and the scaffie were a common sight on the east coast in the 18th Century. What were they?

566 Strathclyde has more miles of motorway than any other Scottish region. Which region comes next?

567 An incredible total of 57 men lost their lives building what?

568 What is bee-baw-babbety?

569 Where is the sprawling council-housing area of Whitfield?

570 Which bridge in Glasgow carries the M8 across the Clyde?

571 Where would you pass over the highest point in the mainline rail network in Scotland?

572 Three hill ranges — the Pentlands, Moorfoots and Lammermuirs — form a continuous west-to-east chain between which two local-authority regions?

573 The distinctive crown steeple of St Giles Cathedral in Edinburgh is not unique. Name the crown-steepled building in Aberdeen?

574 . . . and in Perth?

575 What kind of person is a "clishmaclever"?

576 . . . and a "dubskelper"?

GAME 6
ANSWERS

·GREAT SCOT!·

481 Lossiemouth (in Moray).
482 Sheena Easton.
483 Edinburgh (in 1859).
484 Langholm (it was also his birthplace).
485 Thomas Telford.
486 Fyfe Robertson.
487 Lord Byron.
488 Castaway Alexander Selkirk (who inspired Defoe's *Robinson Crusoe* and Sir Andrew Wood, captain of the *Yellow Carvel*).
489 James Hutton.
490 John Grierson.
491 Robert Burns.
492 William McGonagall.

·MODERN SCOTLAND·

493 Jock Stein.
494 Dougal Haston.
495 *Lanark.*
496 Argyll.
497 Ken Buchanan and Jim Watt.
498 Stuart Henry.
499 Jimmy Reid (during the workers' occupation of the Upper Clyde Shipbuilders yards).
500 Real Madrid.
501 Ardersier (near Inverness).
502 The Orkney Isles (on the small island of Flotta in Scapa Flow).
503 Britt Ekland.
504 Chrissie Hynde.

GAME 6
ANSWERS

·ESTABLISHMENTS·

505 In the North-east (between Peterhead and Fraserburgh).
506 Glasgow School of Art.
507 Thomas Chalmers.
508 Kirkcaldy.
509 Aberdeen.
510 Scottish Secondary Teachers' Association.
511 Northern Lighthouse Board.
512 Aberdeen (in 1945).
513 Lord Advocate.
514 Solicitor-General.
515 New St Andrew's House.
516 Bute House.

·SPORT·

517 Carnoustie Medal (which is criss-crossed by burns of those names).
518 Two (Dundee United and Ayr United).
519 Rangers (he also chose their name, after an English rugby club).
520 Prestwick (in Ayrshire).
521 He was struck by lightning.
522 Alloa ("Wasps") and Queen's Park ("Spiders').
523 Gavin Hastings (his brother was Scott and England were the opposition).
524 Clydebank.
525 Ian McLaughlan.
526 John Jeffrey.
527 Albion Rovers (of Coatbridge).
528 Berwick-upon-Tweed (in England, although Berwick Rangers play in the Scottish League).

GAME 6 ANSWERS

·THE HIGHLANDS & ISLANDS·

529 Strathclyde, Highland, Tayside.
530 Crathes Castle and Crathie Church.
531 Inverewe Gardens (near Gairloch).
532 Fair Isle.
533 The wild cat.
534 The Isle of Lewis.
535 A Corbett.
536 Lord Leverhulme (who purchased Lewis and Harris after the Great War).
537 The red deer.
538 The golden eagle.
539 Arran.
540 Barra.

·HISTORY·

541 Derby.
542 Sir Alexander Mackenzie.
543 The Battle of Largs.
544 Lindisfarne.
545 The Act which banned the wearing of Highland dress.
546 John Knox (the root of the evil was the neck of Mary Queen of Scots).
547 The Porteous Riot (in which the officer Porteous, partly responsible for the hanging, was then hanged by the mob).
548 Freedom.
549 William Wallace.
550 King James IV.
551 Protestant (in 1546).
552 Protestant (they were Covenanters).

GAME 6 ANSWERS

·FROM A' THE AIRTS·

553 Rod Stewart.
554 Liz Lochhead.
555 Folk music.
556 Scottish Ballet.
557 Scone (near Perth).
558 They were both left unfinished.
559 Lerwick, in the Shetlands.
560 Gavin Greig (a schoolmaster).
561 Johnnie Beattie.
562 Jimmy Logan.
563 *On the braes o' Killiecrankie.* (Referring to the battle there in 1689).
564 Cheerful.

·THE LOWLANDS·

565 Types of fishing boat.
566 Central.
567 The Forth Rail Bridge (between 1883 and 1890).
568 A children's game.
569 Dundee.
570 Kingston Bridge.
571 Beattock Summit, 1029′ (314m).
572 Lothian and Borders.
573 King's College.
574 St Leonard's Church (full name, St Leonard's in the Fields).
575 A gossip.
576 A reckless person.

GREAT SCOT!

GAME 7

577 Where did the Irish martyr James Connolly actually come from?

578 Which famous writer was called the "Wizard of the North" and "the Great Unknown"?

579 Where did Mary Queen of Scots spend her last night on Scottish soil?

580 What is the significance of the name Betty Burke in Scottish history?

581 In which battle, the subject of a popular Scottish song, did Jacobite John Graham of Claverhouse, Viscount Dundee, lose his life?

582 Which prime minister became a hero of the Zionists when he said Palestine should become the Jewish homeland?

583 Who founded the world's first savings bank?

584 Of the three great Scots who devoted their lives to exploring Africa — James Bruce, David Livingstone and Mungo Park — only one died in his native land. Which one?

585 Which 19th-century writer was known as the "Ettrick Shepherd"?

586 . . . and which was known as "the Sage of Chelsea"?

587 Which Saint introduced Christianity to South-west Scotland in AD 397?

588 . . . and which 17th-century martyr was finally canonised in 1976?

MODERN SCOTLAND

GAME 7

589 Why did Inverness have a special reason to celebrate on the 23rd of July, 1986?

590 Celtic created a remarkable record in the 1960s and 70s by winning how many consecutive league championships?

591 Which island told TV botanist David Bellamy to get lost?

592 What name was recently given to the new gangs of well-dressed soccer hooligans, like the Rangers Inter City Firm?

593 In 1986, Sir David Smith was appointed to take over from Dr John Burnett as principal of which university?

594 Which similar role was played by Roddy McMillan (as *Pike*) and Mark MacManus (as *Taggart*) in two TV series?

595 Most of the votes in the 1979 devolution referendum were in favour of a Scottish Assembly. Why was it not set up?

596 In which town would you find the prison with the same name as the man who recently took over as manager of a top Scottish football club?

597 The 1970s BBC series *Colditz* was filmed in which castle?

598 . . . and the 1980s STV soap opera *Take The High Road* was filmed on the shores of which loch?

599 In 1972, a group of former Dundee students started a radical Scottish newspaper. What was it called?

600 . . . and in 1975, closure of the Glasgow *Daily Express* plant led to the start of which ill-fated paper?

ESTABLISHMENTS

GAME 7

601 In which coastal town is the Scottish Fisheries Museum?

602 . . . and in which Borders town is the Scottish College of Textiles?

603 What is a "stickit minister"?

604 Dumbreck, Clydesdale and Granville were three of the original members of what?

605 Where would you find Scotland's College of Piping?

606 Which is the oldest and which the youngest of these universities: Glasgow, Dundee and Aberdeen?

607 In which town is the regimental museum of the Black Watch?

608 The holder of which title may grant new coats of arms in Scotland?

609 Where are the studios of the independent radio station NorthSound?

610 . . . and West Sound?

611 How many telephone directories cover Scotland (an error of one is allowed)?

612 . . . and how many Yellow Pages directories (again, an error of one is allowed)?

SPORT

GAME 7

613 Rangers shared the first-ever Scottish League championship with which club?

614 Benny Lynch, Jackie Paterson and Walter McGowan all became world boxing champions — at which weight?

615 The Claret and Amber Club is a supporter's organisation for which football team?

616 Dundee United boss Jim McLean had become the longest-serving premier division manager by the mid 1980s. When did he take over at Tannadice?

617 Which athlete won two silver medals over the 800 metres in the Commonwealth Games and European Championships in 1986?

618 What was the nickname of the now-defunct Glasgow football club, Third Lanark?

619 Two different symbols appear on the Scottish international rugby and soccer strips. What are they?

620 In 1975, England reversed the scoreline by which Scotland's "Wembley Wizards" had beaten them in 1928. What was the score?

621 What is the home town of football club East Fife?

622 . . . and East Stirling?

623 What is the full title of the top British ice hockey team known as the Racers?

624 . . . and the full name of the Rockets?

THE HIGHLANDS & ISLANDS

GAME 7

625 Where would you find the island called "The Dutchman's Cap"?

626 What is the better-known name of Ben Arthur at the head of Loch Long?

627 The "canty and couthy" folk of which island are celebrated in the song *Westering Home*?

628 The Malt Whisky Trail is mapped out to guide tourists round seven distilleries in which local-authority district?

629 Name any two of the three towns in Harris, North Uist and Skye which are linked by ferry?

630 In which local-authority district or districts are the lighthouses at Dunnet Head and Cape Wrath?

631 Many of the works of writer George Mackay Brown are set in the largely imaginary community of Hamnavoe in the Orkney Isles, but where is the real village of Hamnavoe?

632 A simple cairn on the side of Loch Ness recalls which man who died when his speedboat overturned during an attempt on the world water-speed record?

633 The word "firth" does not only denote a wide river-mouth but can also mean an arm of the sea. Which firth separates the Orkney Isles from the mainland?

634 . . . and which firth separates the Isle of Mull from the mainland?

635 Which islands were the birthplaces of the great contemporary Gaelic writer Iain Crichton Smith?

636 . . . and Sorley Maclean?

HISTORY

GAME 7

637 Which famous English author was sent as a spy to Edinburgh by the English Government prior to the Act of Union in 1707?

638 Which constituency in the Highlands and Islands, its boundaries unchanged since 1918, has never returned a Tory MP?

639 King James V was known as "the gaberlunzie man". What is a gaberlunzie?

640 Who were the "Seven Men of Moidart"?

641 Which two cities elected Scotland's first Labour Party MPs in 1906?

642 Which regiment formed "the thin red line" against the Russian cavalry in the Crimea in 1854?

643 Where was Lord Kitchener when he met his end in Hampshire?

644 The year 1566 saw the birth of the Queen's heir at one end of the Royal Mile and the death of the Queen's favourite at the other. Who were they?

645 What was the kingdom established by the Scots in Argyll at the beginning of the 6th century?

646 . . . and which English kingdom pushed the frontier of Anglo-Saxon settlement north to the Firth of Forth, making Lothian their Northernmost province?

647 Rivalry with the "Auld Enemy", is older than Scotland itself. Which side won when the Scots and English clashed at the Battle of Carham in 1018?

648 . . . and when they fought at Solway Moss in 1542?

SECTION 7

FROM A' THE AIRTS

GAME 7

649 How did the weaver-poet Robert Tannahill and Ross-shire writer-geologist Hugh Miller both die?

650 What was the name of Robert Louis Stevenson's sequel to *Kidnapped*?

651 "Stands Scotland where it did?" is a question asked by whom in Shakespeare's *Macbeth*?

652 Robert Louis Stevenson's *Treasure Island* was partly inspired by the novel *Coral Island*. Who wrote it?

653 Which 18th-century artist is best known for his famous portrait of Robert Burns?

654 Which songwriter wrote *The Laird o' Cockpen, The Rowan Tree* and the lament for Bonny Prince Charlie, *Will ye no come back again*?

655 Which vital role in the arts world was first performed by Sir Rudolf Bing and since then by John Drummond and Frank Dunlop?

656 Which Aberdeen housewife "discovered" by folksong collector Hamish Henderson in 1953, went on to establish herself as Scotland's greatest singer of traditional ballads?

657 Who was the lead singer of the 1970s pop group The Tourists?

658 . . . and of Bronski Beat?

659 The traditional heroes of Scottish history have inspired many movies. Who played the leading role in *Bonny Prince Charlie*, (1948)?

660 . . . and in *Rob Roy — The Highland Rogue*, (1953)?

SECTION 8

THE LOWLANDS

GAME 7

661 Where is Scotland's most southerly malt whisky distillery?

662 The traditional Musselburgh pie is simply strips of steak, cooked with what inside them?

663 Which of these towns is not on the River Forth: Alloa, Dunblane, Stirling?

664 In which castle is the Bottle Dungeon?

665 Where did President Eisenhower take up residence when visiting Scotland?

666 What is the geographical origin of the scientific name of the gannet, "sula bassana"?

667 For what very good reason did construction of the Forth Rail Bridge designed by Thomas Bouch, end in 1880?

668 In 1869, the longest railway viaduct in Britain was opened. Which body of water did it cross?

669 In which county is the village of Moscow?

670 . . . and in which county is the village of Houston?

671 Which road crosses the Forth Road Bridge?

672 . . . and which road crosses the Tay Road Bridge?

GAME 7
ANSWERS

·GREAT SCOT!·

577 Edinburgh.
578 Sir Walter Scott.
579 At Dundrennan Abbey, Kirkcudbrightshire.
580 It was a name adopted by Bonny Prince Charlie when he was fleeing the English, disguised as one of Flora Macdonald's maids.
581 Killiecrankie (1689).
582 Arthur Balfour (in the Balfour Declaration).
583 The Rev. Henry Duncan (in his parish of Ruthwell, Dumfries).
584 James Bruce (who discovered the source of the Blue Nile).
585 James Hogg.
586 Thomas Carlyle.
587 St Ninian.
588 St John Ogilvie.

·MODERN SCOTLAND·

589 The Royal wedding took place and Prince Andrew became Earl of Inverness.
590 Nine (1966-74).
591 Islay (where he was attempting to stop Scottish Malt Distillers from cutting peat on the Duich Moss).
592 Soccer Casuals.
593 Edinburgh.
594 Pike was a private eye, while Taggart was a police detective.
595 Because a condition of success was that 40% of the electorate had to vote "Yes", but only 33% did.
596 Inverness (Porterfield Prison — same name as the Aberdeen manager Ian Porterfield).
597 Stirling Castle.
598 Loch Lomond.
599 *The West Highland Free Press* (based in Skye).
600 *The Scottish Daily News* (which lasted just six months).

GAME 7
ANSWERS

·ESTABLISHMENTS·

601 Anstruther.
602 Galashiels.
603 A minister who is licensed to preach, but has not been accepted by any parish.
604 The Scottish Football Association (set up in 1873).
605 Glasgow.
606 Glasgow is the oldest (1451) and Dundee the youngest (1967).
607 Perth (in Balhousie Castle).
608 Lord Lyon King of Arms.
609 Aberdeen.
610 Ayr.
611 Twelve.
612 Seven.

·SPORT·

613 Dumbarton (in 1890-1).
614 Flyweight.
615 Motherwell (claret and amber are their team colours).
616 1971.
617 Tom McKean.
618 The Hi-Hi.
619 A thistle in rugby, a lion in soccer.
620 5-1.
621 Methil.
622 Falkirk.
623 Murrayfield Racers.
624 Dundee Rockets.

GAME 7 ANSWERS

·THE HIGHLANDS & ISLANDS

625 It is one of the Treshnish Isles, west of Mull.
626 The Cobbler.
627 Islay.
628 Moray.
629 Tarbert (Harris), Lochmaddy (North Uist) and Uig (Skye).
630 Dunnet Head is in Caithness, Cape Wrath is in Sutherland.
631 The Shetland Isles.
632 John Cobb (from England, he died in 1952).
633 The Pentland Firth.
634 The Firth of Lorn.
635 Lewis.
636 The island of Raasay (hard by Skye's eastern shore).

·HISTORY·

637 Daniel Defoe (author of *Robinson Crusoe*).
638 Western Isles.
639 A beggar or sorner (he had the habit of wandering through his kingdom, disguised as a commoner).
640 The seven companions who sailed to Scotland with Bonny Prince Charlie to launch the 1745 Jacobite rising.
641 Glasgow and Dundee.
642 The Argyll and Sutherland Highlanders.
643 Off the Orkney Isles (he was aboard HMS *Hampshire* when it went down in 1916).
644 James VI and I (born to Mary in Edinburgh Castle) and David Riccio (Mary's Italian companion, stabbed to death in the Palace of Holyroodhouse).
645 Dalriada.
646 Northumbria.
647 The Scots.
648 The English.

GAME 7
ANSWERS

·FROM A' THE AIRTS·

649 Suicide.
650 *Catriona.*
651 Macduff.
652 R.M. Ballantyne.
653 Alexander Nasmyth.
654 Lady Nairne (born Carolina Oliphant).
655 Director of the Edinburgh Festival.
656 Jeannie Robertson.
657 Annie Lennox.
658 Jimmy Somerville.
659 David Niven.
660 Richard Todd.

·THE LOWLANDS·

661 Bladnoch, near Wigtown in Galloway.
662 Mussels.
663 Dunblane.
664 St Andrews Castle.
665 Culzean Castle (where the uppermost apartments were presented to him as a Scottish residence in 1946).
666 It refers to the Bass Rock (in the Firth of Forth. This is one of the gannets' biggest breeding grounds in Britain).
667 Because Bouch had designed the Tay Rail Bridge which had just disastrously collapsed, killing 77 people.
668 The Solway Firth. It was eventually demolished in 1934.
669 Ayrshire.
670 Renfrewshire.
671 The A90.
672 The A92.

GREAT SCOT!

GAME 8

673 Who was known as "the wisest fool in Christendom"?

674 What was the relationship between writer James Boswell and Margaret Montgomery before they were married in 1769?

675 Which man who gave away much of his worldly wealth said: "A man who dies rich, dies disgraced"?

676 When was the historian Thomas Carlyle born? (Clue: it was one year before Robert Burns died).

677 What outrageous act did Robert the Bruce commit, one month before he was crowned king?

678 Who lost the friendship of poet Hugh MacDiarmid when he declared that Scottish writers should forsake the Scots tongue in favour of English?

679 Who said "Watson, please come here — I want you!", and how did this mark one of the greatest technological advances?

680 Which 11th-century nobleman gained the throne of Scotland with help from the Viking Earl of Orkney?

681 Two Edinburgh men chronicled the histories of other nations. Who wrote *Labour in Irish History*?

682 . . . and who wrote the *History of England* in five volumes?

683 Pop star Annie Lennox and film star Jacqueline Bisset were both born where?

684 Sir Walter Scott and Field-Marshal Earl Haig were both buried in which Abbey?

MODERN SCOTLAND

GAME 8

685 Which pipe band won the world championship six times in a row, from 1981 to 1986?

686 For which Scottish soccer club did George Best play?

687 What resulted from the Wheatley Report?

688 Which leading poet and folksong expert turned down an OBE in 1983?

689 To whom was Liverpool soccer boss Bill Shankly speaking, and on what occasion, when he said, "John, you're immortal".

690 The Grand Slam Year of 1984 was a fitting end to the international rugby career of which Scottish skipper?

691 Denis Nilsen killed and dismembered at least seven young men at his London flat between 1980-83. Where did he come from originally?

692 Who wrote the Scottish soccer squad's 1982 World Cup campaign song, *I have a dream*?

693 Scotland's rural areas have long provided the Liberals with much of their strength. Where was Jo Grimond's seat?

694 . . . and where is David Steel's seat?

695 Skiffler Lonnie Donegan hit number one in 1960 with the ever-popular song *My old man's a . . .*, what?

696 . . . and the Sutherland Brothers and Quiver reached the top five in 1976 with the song *Lying in the arms of . . .*, who?

ESTABLISHMENTS

GAME 8

697 Where is the *John o' Groats Journal* published?

698 After reorganisation in 1975, the town of Keith moved from Banffshire to which district?

699 What do Glasgow University and Edinburgh's St Mary's Episcopal Cathedral have in common?

700 Former Scottish Secretary of State Willie Ross became Lord Ross of Marnock, and Jo Grimond became Baron Grimond of . . . what?

701 Where is BBC Radio Solway based?

702 The regimental museum of the Argyll and Sutherland Highlanders is to be found where?

703 Where is the Scottish Maritime Museum?

704 After the old counties were replaced by regions and districts, only one shire was left in Scotland. Where was it?

705 The Scottish National Portrait Gallery has an unrivalled collection of works by an artist regarded as the master of the portrait medallion in the 18th Century. Who was he?

706 . . . and it also has the largest collection of calotypes by which two pioneering 19th-century photographers?

707 Which major 19th-century railway company had the initials NBR?

708 . . . and which one was GNSR?

SECTION 4

SPORT

GAME 8

709 What is a "caman"?

710 Which Dundee girl won Scotland's only gold medal on the track in the 1986 Commonwealth Games?

711 Which is generally regarded as the oldest surviving golf club in the world?

712 Which Scottish nobleman became a formula one racing driver in 1986?

713 Which rugby club plays at Mansefield Park?

714 What are the easily-confused names of the football grounds of Partick Thistle, Motherwell and East Stirling?

715 On which Ayrshire golf course is the hole called the "Postage Stamp"?

716 The annual clash with England is a highlight of both the rugby and soccer calendars. Which sides came out on top in the first-ever matches in both codes?

717 Celtic have had only six managers since their formation. Name any four of them.

718 . . . and which manager was in charge of Rangers for an incredible total of 34 years?

719 Which Queen's Park footballer, who scored a hat-trick against England in 1900, also established a chain of sweetie shops which outlived him?

720 On which Ayrshire golf course is the "Lang Whang"?

SECTION 5

THE HIGHLANDS & ISLANDS

GAME 8

721 What kind of institution now occupies Lewis Castle in Stornoway on the Isle of Lewis?

722 Which bird is sometimes given the rather inaccurate scientific name of "lagopus scoticus"?

723 Where is the broch or prehistoric round tower known as Mousa?

724 Which writer withdrew to live on the Shetland island of Whalsay?

725 The Gaelic college established in the Isle of Skye in 1973 was not the first such institution. Where is the oldest Gaelic college?

726 The open season for shooting grouse and ptarmigan starts on August 12, the "Glorious Twelfth". But when does it end? (An error of two days is allowed).

727 A series of inexplicable local tragedies was said to have occurred when satanist Aleister Crowley moved into Boleskine House, on the eastern shore of which loch?

728 The Highland Fling is said to mimic the antics of the stag, but what is said to have inspired the dance called the "Sean Trews"?

729 In 1979, Scotland had 114 malt whisky distilleries in operation. To the nearest half dozen, how many were left working by 1986?

730 And where is Scotland's smallest working distillery?

731 Which castle is home to the Earls and Dukes of Sutherland?

732 . . . and what is the fortress of the Clan MacLeod?

HISTORY

733 What dowry did King James III receive when he married Margaret of Denmark in 1472?

734 What is the title of the historical Scottish document which bound its signatories to banish the Catholic Church throughout Britain and Ireland?

735 Which political party held up to five Highland seats between 1885 and 1895?

736 Which playing card is called "the curse of Scotland"?

737 Which company, set up in 1846 to build a rail line from Aberdeen to Inverness, never finished the job but went on to build lines all over the North-east?

738 Two bitter religious enemies were executed at the Mercat Cross outside St Giles Cathedral. One was the 1st Marquis of Argyll, who was the other?

739 The instructions for the massacre of Glencoe stated that the "Old Fox and his Sons do upon no account escape your Hands". The "Old Fox" was the Macdonald chief, but what was his actual surname?

740 William Paterson, the founder of the Bank of England, bankrupted Scotland. How did he achieve this?

741 Who was responsible for the pillaging of Lowland Scotland known as the "Rough Wooing"?

742 . . . and which eligible young woman was he trying to woo?

743 The Romans failed to colonise Scotland, but managed to win the Battle of Mons Graupius. Who led them?

744 . . . and who led the Caledonians?

SECTION 7

FROM A' THE AIRTS

GAME 8

745 Name the three novels which together form the Lewis Grassic Gibbon trilogy *A Scots Quair*.

746 Name the bass guitarist from Bishopbriggs who became a sixties superstar as a member of rock trio Cream?

747 *The Gentle Shepherd* is a pastoral poem written in the Scots tongue, by whom?

748 Willie Clark of Ballindalloch in Moray has emerged as one of the greatest singers of what?

749 Which director was responsible for the films *Whisky Galore* and *The Maggie*?

750 In which city was the renowned Victorian photographer George Washington Wilson mainly based?

751 What is the permanent home of the Edinburgh International Film Festival?

752

The King sits in Dunfermline toun,
Drinking the blude-red wine

These are the opening lines of which poem?

753 The village of Thrums was invented by which author?

754 . . . and who invented the community of Blawearie?

755 In the performing arts, which Scottish national company was formed by Tom Fleming?

756 . . . and which one by Sir Alexander Gibson?

SECTION 8

THE LOWLANDS

GAME 8

757 What kind of woman is a "reekin' lum"?

758 Scotland's first lighthouse was a coal-fired beacon built on the Isle of May in the 17th Century. Where is the Isle of May?

759 What are Jeddart snails and Berwick cockles?

760 Douglas, Isle of Man, is linked by ferry to which Scottish town?

761 What was known both as a "Glasgow magistrate" and a "Dunbar weather"?

762 Near Moffat is a remarkable hollow in the ground, some 500 feet deep. How did it become known as the "Devil's Beeftub"?

763 Who were the Galloway Levellers of 1723?

764 The Ochil Hills form a barrier between which two local-authority regions?

765 A large scale sport and leisure centre is an essential facility in Scotland's New Towns. Where is the Forum?

766 . . . and in which New Town is the Magnum Centre?

767 The expansion of Edinburgh has steadily encroached on other towns. Which historical Burgh was incorporated into the city in 1856?

768 . . . and which Burgh was swallowed up in 1920, and has recently seen the redevelopment of many of its buildings?

GAME 8
ANSWERS

·GREAT SCOT!·

673 James VI and I.
674 They were cousins.
675 Andrew Carnegie.
676 1795.
677 He stabbed John Comyn to death in Greyfriar's monastery in Dumfries.
678 Edwin Muir.
679 Alexander Graham Bell. They were the first words spoken over his new invention — the telephone.
680 Macbeth.
681 James Connolly.
682 David Hume.
683 Aberdeen.
684 Dryburgh Abbey.

·MODERN SCOTLAND·

685 Strathclyde Police Pipe Band.
686 Hibs (season 1979-80).
687 The reorganisation of local government (into region, district and island councils).
688 Hamish Henderson (as a protest against the Tory government's defence policy).
689 To manager Jock Stein, after Celtic had won the European Cup in 1967.
690 Jim Aitken.
691 He was born in Fraserburgh and raised in nearby Strichen.
692 B.A. Robertson.
693 Orkney and Shetland.
694 Tweedale, Ettrick and Lauderdale.
695 . . . *dustman.*
696 . . . *Mary.*

GAME 8
ANSWERS

·ESTABLISHMENTS·

697 Wick.
698 Moray.
699 They were both designed by architect Sir George Gilbert Scott.
700 Firth.
701 Dumfries.
702 Stirling Castle.
703 Irvine (in Ayrshire).
704 Berwickshire District.
705 James Tassie.
706 David Octavius Hill and Robert Adamson.
707 North British Railway.
708 Great North of Scotland Railway.

·SPORT·

709 A shinty stick.
710 Liz Lynch (10,000 metres).
711 The Royal Burgess Golfing Society of Edinburgh, based at Barnton.
712 Johnny Dumfries (the Earl of Dumfries).
713 Hawick.
714 Firhill, Fir Park and Firs Park respectively.
715 Royal Troon.
716 Scotland in the rugby (1871), while it was a no score draw in the soccer in 1872.
717 Willie Maley, Jimmy McStay, Jimmy McGrory, Jock Stein, Billy McNeill, David Hay.
718 William Struth (1920-54).
719 R.S. McColl.
720 Turnberry (the Turnberry Ailsa Course).

GAME 8
ANSWERS

·THE HIGHLANDS & ISLANDS·

721 A technical college.
722 The red grouse (which is unique to Britain rather than Scotland).
723 The Shetland Isles (on the island of Mousa).
724 Hugh MacDiarmid.
725 Canada (the town of St Ann's, in the province of Nova Scotia).
726 December 10th.
727 Loch Ness.
728 From the Gaelic *seann triubhais* (old trousers), the dance expresses the Highlander's contempt of the garb, which they were forced to wear after the failure of the 1745 Jacobite uprising.
729 Eighty-one.
730 Edradour, near Pitlochry, producing 50,000 proof gallons per annum.
731 Dunrobin Castle (near Golspie).
732 Dunvegan Castle (on Skye).

·HISTORY·

733 The Orkney and Shetland Isles (thus ending over 500 years of Norse rule).
734 The Solemn League and Covenant (1643).
735 The Crofter's Party.
736 The nine of diamonds (one explanation is that the orders for the massacre of Glencoe were written on this card).
737 The Great North of Scotland Railway.
738 James Graham, otherwise known as the 1st Marquis of Montrose.
739 MacIain.
740 He invested half of Scotland's capital setting up the Scottish colony at Darien, Panama, which collapsed and brought economic ruin to Scotland, hastening the Union of Parliaments with England.
741 King Henry the VIII of England.
742 Mary Queen of Scots (on behalf of his son Edward).
743 Agricola.
744 Calgacus.

GAME 8
ANSWERS

·FROM A' THE AIRTS·

745 *Sunset Song, Cloud Howe* and *Grey Granite.*
746 Jack Bruce.
747 Allan Ramsay Senior.
748 Bothy Ballads.
749 Alexander Mackendrick.
750 Aberdeen.
751 The Filmhouse Cinema.
752 *Sir Patrick Spens.*
753 J.M. Barrie.
754 Lewis Grassic Gibbon.
755 The Scottish Theatre Company.
756 Scottish Opera.

·THE LOWLANDS·

757 One that nags a lot (the phrase literally means a "smoking chimney")..
758 At the entrance of the Firth of Forth.
759 Types of confectionery.
760 Ardrossan.
761 Salt herring.
762 Because it was formerly used as a pound for stolen cattle.
763 Gangs of evicted farmers who, by night, levelled the new dykes built by the lairds to enclose large beef cattle herds.
764 Tayside and Central.
765 Livingston.
766 Irvine.
767 Canongate.
768 Leith.

GREAT SCOT!

GAME 9

769 Robert Louis Stevenson's *Dr Jekyll and Mr Hyde* was inspired by which respectable Edinburgh figure who led a nocturnal life of burglary and gambling?

770 Which architect designed the Scottish National War Memorial in Edinburgh Castle?

771 Where was African missionary Mary Slessor born?

772 Which 19th-century inventor had the first house in Scotland to be lit by electricity?

773 Which profession did poet Hugh MacDiarmid abandon for journalism?

774 Name "The Tartan Pimpernel".

775 Which college near Edinburgh brought together the two great 20th-century poets from the Orkney Isles?

776 Name the four Scots who have been British prime ministers this century.

777 Name the Edinburgh cemetery where famous 18th century Scots Adam Smith and Robert Fergusson are buried.

778 . . . and name the other Edinburgh kirkyard where the geologist James Hutton and chemist Joseph Black are buried.

779 What do King Charles I and singer Barbara Dickson have in common?

780 . . . and, apart from being small, what do comedian Ronnie Corbett and footballer Gordon Strachan have in common?

MODERN SCOTLAND

GAME 9

781 Which South of Scotland town celebrated its 800th anniversary in 1986?

782 What role did fancamfamina play in Scotland's disastrous 1978 World Cup soccer campaign in Argentina?

783 Which Irish princess made her first sailing from Aberdeen in March 1987?

784 Name the two English heavyweights on the Highland games circuit over the past 30 years, who have both represented Britain in the Olympic shot putt.

785 Scotland's first non-urban railway line since the Beeching cuts opened in 1986. Which two places does it connect?

786 Defeat by Bayern Munich in the 1967 European Cup-Winners' Cup final was made worse for Rangers fans by which event the week before?

787 Why did the number of "drunk and incapable" prosecutions in Aberdeen plummet from 235 in 1983 to only five in 1984?

788 Which region or island area cast the largest percentage of "No" votes in the 1979 devolution referendum?

789 Which was the only football club outside the Old Firm to win the Scottish Cup in the 1960s?

790 . . . and which was the only non-Old Firm club to do it in the 1970s?

791 Mark Knopfler of Dire Straits recorded the sound track for which Scottish film, released in 1983?

792 . . . and which rock band played the soundtrack for the 1985 movie *Restless Natives*?

ESTABLISHMENTS

GAME 9

793 Where are the headquarters of Wigtown District Council?

794 What issue lead to the 1843 Disruption of the General Assembly, and the formation of the Free Church?

795 What exactly do the initials RIAS stand for?

796 The poet Lord Byron was educated at one of the oldest schools in Scotland. Where?

797 Where is the Scottish Lead Mining Museum?

798 Which health board covers the town of Stirling?

799 What is the name of Scottish Opera's small-scale touring company, which performs with simple piano accompaniment?

800 What is the Lantern of the North?

801 Before local government reorganisation, which was the county town of West Lothian?

802 . . . and of Fife?

803 Exactly where are the headquarters of Clackmannan District Council?

804 . . . and of Roxburgh District Council?

SPORT

GAME 9

805 Where can golf be played in the middle of a river?

806 Which event prompted one Scotsman to brandish a banner reading "Alcoholism, not Communism"?

807 Netherdale is the home ground of whch rugby club?

808 Which word did Jimmy Hill use to describe David Narey's spectacular goal against Brazil in the World Cup finals in 1982?

809 What are the names of the two teams which annually contest the traditional Ba' game through the streets of Kirkwall?

810 Who is the only footballer to score a hat-trick in a Scottish League Cup final and still end up on the losing side?

811 The 14-11 victory over the English Rugby team in 1925 clinched the Grand Slam for Scotland, but what was the other historic feature of that game?

812 If Hamilton footballers are Academicals, what are Forres footballers?

813 Which sport is played by Ayr Burners?

814 . . . and Ayr Bruins?

815 Which football club has its address in Albion Road?

816 . . . and in Kerrydale Street?

SECTION 5

THE HIGHLANDS & ISLANDS

GAME 9

817 In which North-east fishing village is the ceremony of Burning the Clavie held every New Year?

818 Which is the only Scottish castle with a circular courtyard?

819 For what purpose was Tobermory built in the late 18th Century?

820 Where was Britain's most northerly coalmine, which closed in 1974?

821 The word "mod" has become part of the English language since it was adopted for the national Gaelic festival. But what is its Gaelic meaning?

822 What is the main town in South Uist?

823 The magic of which island is celebrated in the song *The Lights of Loch Indaal*?

824 "Doolies" is the name given to people from which Ross-shire fishing village, famous for its unique dialect?

825 Which is the highest mountain in the Outer Hebrides?

826 . . . and the highest mountain on Arran?

827 Which world-famous commodity is named after the Gaelic word for "water"?

828 . . . and which common English word comes from the Gaelic meaning "in plenty"?

HISTORY

GAME 9

829 Who carried out the "Herschip of Buchan", the burning and looting campaign described as "the most merciless devastation the North-east has ever known"?

830 Who was the Sovereign at the time of the Union of Parliaments in 1707?

831 Which regiment made the famous cavalry charge at Waterloo in 1815?

832 Celebrations were held in 1985 at the village of Dunnichen, near Forfar, to mark the 1300th anniversary of which battle?

833 How did the steam locomotive called "The Diver", which was scrapped in 1919, earn its nickname?

834 Which Highland constituency has been held by the Conservatives, an independent Conservative, the Liberals, Labour and the SDP — all since the 1950s?

835 The "Knights Baronet" scheme was devised under King James VI and I to encourage settlement of which area?

836 After the departure of the Romans, where did the Britons of Strathclyde establish their capital?

837 Few Scottish kings died in bed — which one died when he fell from his stumbling horse on a Fife clifftop?

838 . . . and which one died in a siege of Roxburghe Castle when a cannon blew up in his face?

839 On which day did the old Celtic year begin?

840 . . . and which day was known in Scots as "Hunt-the-Gowk" day?

SECTION 7

FROM A' THE AIRTS

GAME 9

841 Which major artist died aboard ship while returning from Jerusalem, and for whom his contemporary Turner painted *Peace — Burial at Sea* as a tribute?

842 Which leading 20th-century artist spent her later years painting the wild coastline around the North-east village of Catterline?

843 In 1787, Robert Burns commissioned a tombstone in memory of a poet whom he hailed as "by far my elder brother in muse". Which poet?

844 Where do players of the bagpipes compete for the ultimate prize in solo piping, the Gold Clasp?

845 According to the folksong *Macpherson's Rant*, in which town was the clock altered to make sure Macpherson was hanged before he could be reprieved?

846 Which socialist theatre company set out in the 1940s to be "the Scottish People's Theatre"?

847 Which play was revived to critical acclaim at the 1948 Edinburgh Festival, having not been staged for over 400 years?

848 Name the dead rock 'n' roll singer played by Robbie Coltrane in the 1987 TV series *Tutti Frutti*.

849 Who was the wife of poet Robert Burns?

850 . . . and of historian Thomas Carlyle?

851 Which Scots film featured five Hebrideans who refused to pay their road tax?

852 . . . and which one was inspired by the sinking of the SS *Politician* near Eriskay?

THE LOWLANDS

GAME 9

853 What is the main ingredient of the broth known as Powsowdie?

854 Which town once had 32 distilleries, of which only two now remain?

855 What was a buttock-mail?

856 In which town does the Theatre Royal stand on Shakespeare Street?

857 A man named Cowan might be expected to build what?

858 Which of these towns is not on the river Tweed: Selkirk, Melrose or Peebles?

859 Which major Scots literary work was first published in 1983, sixteen years after the death of its translator, W.L. Lorimer?

860 What is the Scots name given to the brooch, usually in the shape of a heart or two hearts entwined, and given as a token of love or betrothal?

861 Castles are perched in some precarious coastal locations. Where is Tantallon Castle?

862 And which coastal castle was surrendered in 1547 after an attack by the French Navy, which took John Knox prisoner?

863 "Gowk", when applied to a person, means a fool, but what does it mean when applied to a bird?

864 . . . and "tammie norrie", when applied to a person, means a shy fellow but what does it mean when applied to a bird?

GAME 9
ANSWERS

·GREAT SCOT!·

769 Deacon Brodie.
770 Sir Robert Lorimer.
771 Aberdeen (although she grew up in Dundee).
772 Lord Kelvin.
773 Teaching.
774 Donald Caskie (a minister in occupied France during World War II, sentenced to death by the Germans for helping British fugitives, then reprieved).
775 Newbattle Abbey (an adult education college, where warden Edwin Muir helped launch the career of student George Mackay Brown).
776 Arthur Balfour, Sir Henry Campbell-Bannerman, James Ramsay Macdonald and Sir Alec Douglas-Home.
777 Canongate Churchyard.
778 Greyfriar's Churchyard.
779 They were both born in Dunfermline.
780 They were both born in Edinburgh.

·MODERN SCOTLAND·

781 Dumfries.
782 It was the drug taken by Willie Johnston (an offence for which he was sent home early).
783 *St Sunniva* (the new Orkney and Shetland ferry, named after a 10th-century princess).
784 Arthur Rowe (in the 60s and 70s) and Geoff Capes (in the 80s).
785 Edinburgh and Bathgate.
786 Celtic winning the European Cup.
787 Because of the opening of Scotland's first detoxification centre at Albyn House.
788 The Shetland Isles.
789 Dunfermline.
790 Aberdeen.
791 *Local Hero*.
792 Big Country.

GAME 9
ANSWERS

·ESTABLISHMENTS·

793 Stranraer.
794 The laird's right to appoint the minister in each of his parishes.
795 Royal Incorporation of Architects in Scotland.
796 Aberdeen Grammar School.
797 Wanlockhead (Dumfriesshire).
798 Forth Valley.
799 Opera Go Round.
800 Elgin Cathedral.
801 Linlithgow.
802 Cupar.
803 Alloa.
804 Hawick.

·SPORT·

805 Perth (King James VI course, established in 1858, is on Moncrieffe Island in the River Tay).
806 The Scotland-USSR soccer match in the 1982 World Cup finals (a 2-2 draw).
807 Gala.
808 "Toepoke".
809 Uppies and Doonies.
810 Joe Harper of Hibs (who lost to Celtic 6-3 in season 1974-75).
811 It was the first game played at Murrayfield.
812 Mechanics (Forres Mechanics is the name of the Highland League team).
813 American Football.
814 Ice Hockey.
815 Hibs (in Edinburgh).
816 Celtic (in Glasgow).

GAME 9
ANSWERS

·THE HIGHLANDS & ISLANDS·

817 Burghead.
818 Rothesay Castle (Isle of Bute).
819 As a fisheries port, by the British Fisheries Society.
820 Brora (Sutherland).
821 A law court (held by a chieftain).
822 Lochboisdale.
823 Islay.
824 Avoch (pronounced "Och").
825 The Clisham, Isle of Harris, 2620 feet (875m).
826 Goat Fell, 2868 feet (799m).
827 Whisky (from "uisge").
828 Galore (from "gu leor").

·HISTORY·

829 Robert the Bruce.
830 Queen Anne.
831 The Royal Scots Greys.
832 The Battle of Nechtansmere (when the Northumbrians were defeated by the Picts).
833 It was the Tay Rail Bridge disaster train which was salvaged and returned to service.
834 Caithness and Sutherland.
835 Nova Scotia, in Canada. (Any laird who could provide both emigrants and money, received the title Baronet of Nova Scotia in return).
836 Dumbarton.
837 Alexander III (in 1286).
838 James II (in 1460).
839 October 31st (Halloween).
840 April 1st (A gowk is a fool).

GAME 9 ANSWERS

·FROM A' THE AIRTS·

841 Sir David Wilkie (1785-1841).
842 Joan Eardley.
843 Robert Fergusson.
844 Inverness.
845 Banff (a "Scottish Robin Hood", hanged in 1700).
846 Glasgow Unity Theatre.
847 *Ane Satyre of the Thrie Estaitis*, by Sir David Lindsay.
848 Big Jazza.
849 Jean Armour.
850 Jane Welsh.
851 *Laxdale Hall* (1952).
852 *Whisky Galore* (1949).

·THE LOWLANDS·

853 A sheep's head.
854 Campbeltown.
855 A fine imposed on a person for sexual immorality.
856 Dumfries.
857 A drystane dyke, since a "cowan" was a dyker.
858 Selkirk.
859 *The New Testament in Scots.*
860 A luckenbooth.
861 North Berwick.
862 St Andrews Castle.
863 A cuckoo.
864 A puffin, since a shy fellow has the same problem as a puffin on the Bass Rock:

Tammie Norrie o' the Bass
Canna kiss a bonny lass.

SECTION 1

GREAT SCOT!

GAME 10

865 "This is far stronger and better than ether" was said by which famous Scot as he regained consciousness?

866 Which Clydebank-born journalist won the Pulitzer prize and wrote his own column for the *New York Times*?

867 Where was Orkney novelist Eric Linklater actually born?

868 An area of Mars is named after a Scot whose portrait was the only one Einstein had in his study. Who?

869 Whose last words were "Do I look strange?"?

870 Which important job in the local community was held by the fathers of Hugh MacDiarmid and George Mackay Brown?

871 John Boyd Dunlop is often associated with the invention of the pneumatic tyre, but an India rubber tyre had already been patented by whom?

872 Which great writer had a job as keeper of the Advocate's Library in Edinburgh?

873 Which king was the first to rule over both Picts and Scots?

874 . . . and which queen introduced both the English language and the Roman church to the Scottish people?

875 Who died, shouting "I am a priest!"?

876 . . . and who died, claiming "Now it is come!"?

MODERN SCOTLAND

GAME 10

877 Who said this of Robert Burns in 1965?
They told me his work was very, very neat,
So I replied: 'But who did he ever beat?'

878 Where is the smallest international airport in Britain?

879 Who founded the Scottish Baroque Ensemble in 1969?

880 Which major golf championship was revived in 1986 after a 13 year break?

881 Which band once included Billy Connolly and Gerry Rafferty, long before they became world-famous?

882 Which world champion boxer was killed in a South African streetfight in 1966?

883 Which Gallery director mounted an unsuccessful public appeal to raise £8.25 million to buy the painting called *The Adoration of the Magi*?

884 What was unusual about the USA duo who won the 1984 World Bowls pairs title in Aberdeen?

885 Which Scottish comedian appeared in the 1967 James Bond film *Casino Royale*?

886 . . . and another appeared in the 1983 thriller *Gorky Park*. Who was he?

887 Police have never solved the mysterious disappearance of an Inverness woman and her three year old son, on the same day that her BMW was found gutted by fire in a Highland lay-by. What was her name?

888 . . . and who was the student, whose disappearance in 1981 from a Himalayan village started her father on a seemingly hopeless search for her?

ESTABLISHMENTS

GAME 10

889 A cynical saying goes: "There's nae place like hame, said the devil when he found himself in the. . .", what?

890 What is the historical distinction achieved by the *Mercurius Caledonius*?

891 Where are the headquarters of the Argyll and Bute District Council?

892 What was the name of the 19th-century railway company known affectionately as the "Sou' West"?

893 What is the title of the chief criminal judge in Scotland?

894 The town of Callander was in the old county of Perthshire. Which district is it in now?

895 Where is BBC Radio Tweed located?

896 Name the London HQ of the Scottish Office?

897 Several universities have their own arts centres. Which one is part of St Andrews University?

898 . . . and which one is part of Stirling University?

899 Which Canadian University was founded by the Rev. C.F. MacKinnon?

900 . . . and which one was set up in 1921 from a bequest left by a Glasgow-born fur trader?

SECTION 4

SPORT

GAME 10

901 "It is an intensely Presbyterean activity . . . you do not play against an opponent. You may play alongside one." What is writer Cliff Hanley describing?

902 Name four of the five Scottish League football teams whose full name begins and ends with the same letter.

903 What is special about Dale Golf course?

904 What makes the name of St Johnstone football club unique in British football?

905 Name both of Scotland's first rugby and soccer clubs.

906 What two things do football clubs Liverpool and Stirling Albion have in common?

907 What do Open golf champion Tom Morris Jr and world darts champion Jocky Wilson have in common?

908 Four football clubs share the distinction of having the biggest pitch in Scotland, 115 by 75 yards. Rangers is one of them, name two of the other three.

909 Where is the Valley of Sin?

910 . . . and where is Tel-el-Kebir?

911 During the 1950s, top-class players helped both of Edinburgh's major clubs to rival Glasgow's Old Firm for football honours. Name the "Famous Five" forward line of Hibs.

912 . . . and the "Terrible Trio" strikeforce of Hearts.

THE HIGHLANDS & ISLANDS

GAME 10

913 An old Highland saying goes, "Speek weel o' the Hielands, but dwell in the Laigh". Where is the Laigh?

914 Where is the Clan Macpherson Museum?

915 Near which town was there a goldrush in 1896?

916 In 1958 Strathy Point was the last manned lighthouse to be built in Scotland. Where is it?

917 Hell's Glen runs between two Argyll lochs — name either of them?

918 What is the nickname given to the three buildings standing side-by-side in the centre of Aberdeen — The Central Library, St Mark's Church and His Majesty's Theatre?

919 A gaelic proverb tells of three thefts of which a Highlander is never ashamed — name one of them.

920 Each September, the menfolk of the parish of Ness in Lewis sail 40 miles north to the isolated rocks of Sula Sgeir for a three-week cull of the gugas. What type of bird is a guga?

921 What is caboc?

922 . . . and what is carrageen?

923 Which island town has a main thoroughfare with the unlikely name of Cromwell Street?

924 . . . and which island town has a street with the even less likely name of Khyber Pass?

HISTORY

GAME 10

925 To which period of Scottish history does this saying refer, "Ding doon the nests and the rooks will flee awa' "?

926 Which town elected Scotland's first Communist MP and first Scottish Nationalist MP?

927 On which Scottish railway line was a steam locomotive first used?

928 Why did the devout Queen Margaret establish a ferry across the Firth of Forth, between the places still known as North and South Queensferry?

929 As he lay dying, Sir Walter Scott was said to have whispered: "My wound is deep, I am fain to sleep". Whose words was he quoting?

930 What age was Bonnie Prince Charlie when defeated at Culloden in 1746?

931 Which Scottish settler drove in the last spike of the Canadian Pacific Railway, which he had financed?

932 The name "Fife Adventurers" was given to the settlers sent by King James VI in 1598, to establish a colony in which hostile place?

933 What was the real name of Lady MacBeth, wife of Scotland's 11th-century king?

934 . . . and what was the equally colourful name of her simpleton son?

935 Who set out to sack Aberdeen in 1411, but decided to go home after the indecisive Battle of Harlaw?

936 . . . and who did sack Aberdeen in 1644, after the defenders of the city had shot a drummer boy under a flag of truce?

FROM A' THE AIRTS

GAME 10

937 "Whaur's yer Willie Shakespeare noo?" was the comment shouted by a member of the audience during a performance of which play in the 18th century?

938 How and where did Will Fyffe, the comedian who wrote the song *I belong to Glasgow,* die?

939 In literature, who was Isobel Guthrie?

940 Which poet completed the first full-length translation of a major Latin text in Britain?

941 Mendelssohn's *Hebrides Overture* was inspired by Fingal's Cave on Staffa, but which building inspired his *Scotch Symphony*?

942 Which infamous Judge inspired Robert Louis Stevenson's *Weir of Hermiston*?

943 Why did the City of Edinburgh have cause to regret the confiscation of ornamental railings, from Hutton Castle in Berwickshire, to help the Second World War effort?

944 Which were the two major civic theatres which first opened within five days of each other in 1906, both showing pantomimes?

945 Name the council-owned art gallery in Greenock?

946 . . . and in Milngavie, on Glasgow's outskirts?

947 Which poet wrote *The Queen's Wake*?

948 . . . and which one wrote *The Kingis Quair* (the title gives a clue)?

SECTION 8

THE LOWLANDS

GAME 10

949 Which city was Robert Louis Stevenson describing when he wrote: "From their smoky beehives, ten storeys high, the unwashed look down upon the open squares and gardens of the wealthy"?

950 Name all five Edinburgh streets, which together are known as The Royal Mile?

951 A "soor ploom" is a kind of confectionery, but where would a someone described as a "soor ploom" come from?

952 Which River joins the Tweed at Kelso?

953 What does the Scots word *baudrons* mean?

954 The Common Riding ceremony of which Borders town commemorates the day when 80 townsmen rode to fight at Flodden, and only one returned?

955 Which is the name given to all hills in the Lowlands over 2000 feet high?

956 How long is a Scotch mile?

957 In which Borders town is the standard-bearer leading the annual Common Riding known as the "Braw Lad"?

958 . . . and in which town is he the "Callant"?

959 Who keeps Sir Walter Scott company on Princes Street?

960 . . . and who did Greyfriar's Bobby keep company in Greyfriar's Kirkyard?

GAME 10
ANSWERS

·GREAT SCOT!·

865 Sir James Young Simpson, having invented, and just tried, chloroform for the first time.

866 James Reston.

867 Wales.

868 James Clerk Maxwell (1831-1879), the father of modern physics.

869 Robert Louis Stevenson (Samoa, 1894).

870 The Postman.

871 R.W. Thompson (from Stonehaven).

872 David Hume (the 19th-century philosopher).

873 Kenneth MacAlpin.

874 Queen Margaret (wife of Malcolm Canmore).

875 Cardinal Beaton (as he was stabbed to death in 1546).

876 John Knox (1572).

·MODERN SCOTLAND·

877 Muhammad Ali.

878 Kirkwall (when a service to Norway was started).

879 Leonard Friedman.

880 The Scottish Open.

881 The Humblebums.

882 Jackie Paterson (world flyweight champion).

883 Timothy Clifford (director of the National Galleries of Scotland).

884 One of them was a Scot, George Adrain, supplied by the hosts as a last minute replacement for an injured American).

885 Chic Murray.

886 Rikki Fulton.

887 Renee MacRae (who vanished in 1976).

888 Alison MacDonald (who vanished in 1981).

GAME 10 ANSWERS

·ESTABLISHMENTS·

889 ". . . the Court of Session".
890 The first Scottish newspaper (started and finished in 1661).
891 Lochgilphead.
892 The Glasgow and South Western Railway.
893 The Lord Justice General.
894 Stirling.
895 Selkirk.
896 Dover House.
897 The Crawford Arts Centre.
898 The MacRobert Centre.
899 St Francis Xavier University (in Nova Scotia, 1853).
900 McGill University (in Ontario, with money left by James McGill).

·SPORT·

901 Golf.
902 Celtic, Dundee United, East Fife, East Stirlingshire, Kilmarnock.
903 The most northerly course in Britain (three miles from Lerwick).
904 It is the only senior club in Britain which includes the letter "J"
905 Rugby was Edinburgh Academicals (1857), while soccer was Queen's Park (10 years later).
906 They both play at grounds called Annfield (Liverpool's ground is spelt with one 'n'), and they were both managed by the Shankly brothers — Bob at Stirling and Bill at Liverpool.
907 They were both born in St Andrews.
908 Arbroath, Kilmarnock and Queen's Park.
909 The Old Course, St Andrews (a feature of the 18th hole).
910 Troon (the seventh hole was made just after the battle of that name in the Sudan in 1882).
911 Gordon Smith, Bobby Johnstone, Lawrie Reilly, Eddie Turnbull and Willie Ormond.
912 Alfie Conn, Willie Bauld and Jimmy Wardhaugh.

GAME 10
ANSWERS

·THE HIGHLANDS & ISLANDS·

913 Moray (the Laigh of Moray is the low land in the north of the district).
914 Newtonmore.
915 Helmsdale.
916 Sutherland (on the north coast).
917 Loch Goil and Loch Fyne.
918 Education, Salvation and Damnation.
919 A branch from the wood, a fish from the river and a deer from the mountain.
920 A young gannet.
921 A cheese (double-cream cheese, rolled in oatmeal).
922 A seaweed, which forms the basis of a dessert.
923 Stornoway (Lewis).
924 Stromness (Orkney).

·HISTORY·

925 The Reformation (referring to the razing of ecclesiastical buildings, and the fleeing of the priests).
926 Motherwell (Communist in 1922, Nationalist in 1945).
927 The Kilmarnock and Troon line (in 1817).
928 To encourage pilgrims from Lothian to visit St Andrews in Fife.
929 James, Earl of Douglas (as he lay dying at the Battle of Otterburn, 1388).
930 Twenty-five.
931 Donald Smith (later Lord Strathcona).
932 The Isle of Lewis (the colonists were massacred).
933 Gruoch.
934 Lulach.
935 The Lord of the Isles, Donald Macdonald.
936 James Graham, otherwise known as the 1st Marquis of Montrose.

GAME 10 ANSWERS

·FROM A' THE AIRTS·

937 *Douglas*, by the Rev. John Home, who was thrown out of his parish by the Kirk for dabbling in "devillish" playwriting.

938 He fell out of a hotel window in St Andrews.

939 Christopher Grieve (whose pseudonyms included Isobel Guthrie and Hugh MacDiarmid).

940 Gavin Douglas (who translated Virgil's *Aeneid* into Scots).

941 The Abbey of Holyroodhouse (not the palace).

942 Lord Braxfield (who said "Hang a thief when he's young, and he'll no steal when he's auld").

943 The embittered owner William Burrell presented his art collection to Glasgow instead.

944 His Majesty's in Aberdeen and the King's Theatre in Edinburgh (3rd and 8th December).

945 The McLean Art Gallery.

946 The Lillie Art Gallery.

947 James Hogg.

948 King James I of Scotland.

·THE LOWLANDS·

949 Edinburgh, in particular the towering Old Town tenements.

950 From the top: Castlehill, Lawnmarket, High Street, Canongate, Abbey Strand.

951 Galashiels.

952 The Teviot.

953 A cat.

954 Selkirk. (The sorrowful waving of a flag by the survivor is recalled by the Casting of the Flag ceremony).

955 Donalds (named after Percy Donald, who listed them).

956 1984 yards (1815m).

957 Galashiels.

958 Jedburgh.

959 His favourite hound Maida, who sits at his feet on the Scott Monument.

960 John Gray (the faithful terrier kept watch over his master's grave until he too died).

SECTION 1

SCOTS ABROAD

GAME 11

961 In which American town was the first St Andrew's Society formed in 1729?

962 Where in the United States are the oldest and largest Highland Games held?

963 By which Scottish name was the Vanuata group of South Pacific islands previously known?

964 Which 18th-century Scot held officer's rank in the British, American and Russian Navys and professed himself "a citizen of the world"?

965 What unusual event takes place in May at Pittsfield, Massachusetts?

966 In which country will you find Port Douglas and Port Pirie, and the Rivers Mitchell and Murray?

967 The first club of its type in the USA was called St Andrews of Yonkers. What type of club was this?

968 Where are the Scottish Nova Scotian Descendants Association based?

969 Which Australian state capital was named after a Scottish town?

970 . . . and which was named after a Scottish soldier and governor?

971 Which Scot became the first Prime Minister of Canada in 1867?

972 . . . and which Canadian, brought up in Scotland, became British Prime Minister in 1922?

SECTION 2

SPOKEN ABOUT SCOTLAND

GAME 11

Who said these things, both good and bad, about Scotland?

973 "The noblest prospect which a Scotsman ever sees is the high road that leads him to England".

974 "It is never difficult to distinguish between a Scotsman with a grievance, and a ray of sunshine."

975 A female novelist: ". . . the Scotch have melancholy in their bones . . . being entirely without frivolity."

976 A former British Prime Minister: "The Scots have only got one bad fault — there are too few of them."

977 An American: "Every line of strength in American history is a line coloured with Scottish blood."

978 A famous Scots socialist: "Scotland must again have independence — the communism of the clans must be re-established on a modern basis."

979 Another left-wing Scot: "The Scottish Dukes . . . still hold sway, owning thousands of acres and clinging to feudal landed power that was won by men with the morals of tomcats."

980 An English 20th-century writer: "In some areas, at any rate, Scotland is almost an occupied country".

981 A 19th-century composer: "I once . . . closed my eyes and then correctly stated that five Highlanders had passed — my nose had seen them".

982 A contemptuous Englishman speaking about oats: "A grain, which in England is generally given to horses, but in Scotland supports the people."

983 "I do indeed come from Scotland, but I cannot help it."

984 And lastly, a Frenchman: "It is from Scotland that we receive rules of taste in all the arts."

SECTION 3

WHAT'S IN A NAME?

GAME 11

The words used to describe jobs which existed centuries ago have been passed down to us in the form of names. Give the original meaning of these Scots' names.

985 Webster.

986 Souter.

987 Baxter.

988 Mair.

989 Stoddart.

990 Durward.

991 Dewar.

992 Dempster.

993 Lorimer.

994 Caird.

995 Baird.

996 Gow.

THE DRAM-WINNER!

997 Name the link between Reg Dwight and David Toulmin.

998 What have Fortingall and the Royal Scots in common?

999 Which similar positions were held by entertainer Will Starr and rock singer Ian Anderson?

Try winning a case of Dalmore malt whisky in time for Hogmanay 1987! Just give your answers to the last three questions and send to the addressee on the other side.

997 ....

998 ....

999 ....

GAME 11 ANSWERS

·SCOTS ABROAD·

961 Charleston, South Carolina.

962 The Grandfather Mountain Games, in the Blue Ridge Mountains of North Carolina, first held in 1956.

963 New Hebrides.

964 Paul Jones, founder of the American Navy.

965 An indoor Highland Games.

966 Australia.

967 A golf club.

968 New Zealand, their forefathers journeyed from Scotland, through Canada and Australia before settling in new Zealand.

969 Perth.

970 Brisbane. After Sir Thomas Brisbane.

971 John A. MacDonald, born in Glasgow.

972 Andrew Bonar Law.

·SPOKEN ABOUT SCOTLAND·

973 Dr Samuel Johnson.

974 P.G. Wodehouse.

975 Virginia Woolf, in a letter of 1938.

976 David Lloyd George.

977 Woodrow Wilson.

978 John MacLean, socialist leader, in a pamphlet of 1920.

979 Willie Hamilton, MP.

980 George Orwell in *The Tribune*.

981 Felix Mendelssohn.

982 Dr Samuel Johnson, speaking to his biographer James Boswell.

983 James Boswell. Johnson replied: "That, Sir, I find, is what a very great many of your countrymen cannot help."

984 Voltaire.

·WHAT'S IN A NAME?·

985 A weaver.

986 A cobbler, or shoemaker.

987 A baker.

988 A law officer.

989 A herdsman of bullocks (or "stot herd").

990 A doorkeeper (or "door ward").

991 The keeper of a Saint's relic.

992 The court officer who pronounced the judge's sentence (also called "doomster").

993 A maker of metal parts of a horse's harness.

994 A tinker.

995 A poet (or "Bard").

996 A blacksmith (from the Gaelic for blacksmith, "gobha").

Name..

Address..

....

.... Postcode........................

I certify that I am over 18 years old

Signed .... Date........................

Send this coupon before 24th December 1987 to:

PROMOTIONS

LOCHAR PUBLISHING

BANKHEAD

MOFFAT DG10 9LS

The winner will be drawn on the 29th December 1987